On her wedding day, Tara was abducted by the masterful Leon Petrides, dragged off to Greece and forced to marry him. And he had seen to it that there was no possibility of escape—so she knew it would be a waste of time trying to get away. Or was it because, after all, she didn't really want to go?

# PAGAN LOVER

BY

ANNE HAMPSON

MILLS & BOON LIMITED
LONDON W1

First published 1980
Australian copyright 1980
Philippine copyright 1980
This edition 1980

© Anne Hampson 1980

ISBN 0 263 73267 3

Set in Linotype Baskerville

Made and printed in Great Britain by
Richard Clay (The Chaucer Press), Ltd., Bungay, Suffolk

# CHAPTER ONE

THERE was a look of serene contentment on Tara Bennet's face as she listened to the voice coming over the line. Her fiancé never failed to telephone her at this time every day, just to remind her, he teased, that she was his and his alone, and woe betide her if she allowed any of her male patients to flirt with her.

'What are the present bunch like?' David wanted to know.

'We have two new patients; they came in last night very late. Had an accident with a car. I didn't see them until this morning, of course, when I came on duty. One's a Greek, and is he arrogant! I haven't spoken to him yet—in fact, he and I haven't even exchanged glances. But Sue's furious at the way he treats her. Anyone would think he was a god, she says.' Tara laughed as she spoke, thinking of Sue's furious expression when she came away from the private ward in which the Greek was accommodated.

'What's he like?'

'Handsome, so Sue says. About thirty-two, she thinks, but he refused to give his age.' Tara laughed again before going on to tell her fiancé what the Greek said to Sue when she asked him his age. He had looked at her arrogantly and snapped,

'What the devil has that to do with you? Get on with your job and stop asking irrelevant questions!'

'There's obviously nothing seriously wrong with him,' observed David.

'No, but the doctor on duty insisted on his having an X-ray because it was rather a nasty accident, with this Greek being hit by a car travelling on the wrong side of the road, and the Greek being thrown out on to the hard standing. He's very bruised and has a deep cut on his head.'

David changed the subject abruptly.

'I forgot to tell you, my love, that we're invited to supper at Mary's on Friday. John's home on leave at last.'

'Lovely! He'll be at the wedding, then?'

'I should think so. He's been overseas for two years so I expect his leave will be a fairly long one.' David paused a moment. 'Only nine days before we're together. Tara, I can hardly wait.'

She was so happy that words failed her for the moment. It was an interlude of silence during which both she and he became deep in thoughts of the future which, as far as Tara could see, was roses and red wine all the way. She was glad that David's brother would be at the wedding, as she herself had no relatives at all, and so the close relatives were all on David's side. And as he had very few—just his parents, his brother and a couple of aged aunts—it was a happy circumstance that John would be able to attend the wedding.

'I shall have to go now,' Tara was saying presently. 'Sue's going off duty and I'm taking her place.'

'Watch that Greek, then,' he warned teasingly. 'They've got a reputation for being womanisers.'

'Well, this one isn't! Sue's here now, making faces and thumbing in the direction of the private ward where the Greek is.'

'It takes a lot to get Sue riled, doesn't it?'

'Usually, yes. She's the most placid person—ideally fitted to be a nurse.'

'Like you, my love. 'Bye for now; see you tonight.'

The receiver clicked; Tara looked at Sue and grimaced.

'He's an arrogant pig!' declared Sue, and for a moment Tara could only stare at her, for Sue never

ever said things like that about patients, no matter how much they tried her patience.

'And I've got to take over from you,' said Tara at last. 'I'm certainly not looking forward to it!'

'He wants to go out, but Doctor Jameson left strict orders that he's to be kept under observation for a while.'

'We can't keep him in if he wants to leave. Doctor Jameson knows this as well as we do.'

'It seems that Doctor Jameson's not satisfied that some internal injury might not have resulted from the accident.'

Tara nodded but said nothing, and a few minutes later she was entering the private ward, carrying a tray on which was a cup of coffee and some biscuits. She had actually hesitated outside the door, annoyed to find that her heartbeats had increased rather uncomfortably.

The Greek was standing by the window, staring out, and for a fleeting moment Tara looked at him from the back view. So tall! And with broad shoulders and a slim waist; no surplus weight carried on an athletic body like that, was Tara's instant conclusion. He turned, slowly, and for another fleeting moment she saw him in profile. Classical lines that reminded her of some Greek statues she had seen in the museum, statues sculptured in stone. She noted the dominant chin, the flexed line of the jaw, the aquiline nose....

He was facing her ... and something jerked at her nerves. Those eyes, black, surely, and as hard as pitch-blende! They fixed hers, then widened slowly, piercing in their intense scrutiny. The man seemed mesmerised for a space, as if he were observing something that was quite beyond belief.

'Your—your coffee,' stammered Tara, but she made no move to place the tray on the table. Her legs felt weak, her mind confused. There was something akin to

an electric current running round and round the room,
passing between her and the man standing there, his
lean unsmiling face turned to hers. She vaguely noticed
the very dark skin, the prominent cheekbones, the
typical low forehead of the Greeks, the strong black
hair, thick and crisp and swept back as if he had ruthlessly attempted to straighten out the natural wave.
She was thinking of Sue's statement that the man was
handsome and shook her head, rejecting the idea.
There was too much arrogance in his features, and inflexible qualities which mingled with an unmistakable
harshness and air of superiority.

Tara decided that she had never before seen such an
arresting face ... nor a more formidable one. No, he
was not handsome—at least, not to her way of thinking. David now ... he was not so tall, granted, but his
features were soft and kind and his eyes were frank and
open. His mouth was full, denoting compassion—not
like this man's mouth which was thin, cruel—and yet
at the same time there was about it a sensual quality
that caused an involuntary shiver to trickle along
Tara's spine. She would not care to find herself alone
with him !

He continued to stare at her in silence, absorbing
things of which Tara was not wholly unaware—the
rare beauty of her features with their delicate contours,
the retroussé nose, the lovely rosy lips, slightly parted
as if inviting a tender, reverent kiss. Her vivid blue
eyes were startled, because of the sensation within her
which she could not have understood even if she had
been clear-minded enough to try. Her long dark lashes
fluttered down as she attempted to hide her expression
from him; the soft sweep of colour that came to her
cheeks could not possibly be hidden. Tara bit her lip,
wondering why she had no power to speak, why she
was unable to move towards the table and deposit the
tray.

The Greek spoke at last, but the relief of the silence being broken gave way instantly to an inexplicable wave of apprehension as she heard the odd inflection which edged his voice, a finely-timbred voice which carried the merest hint of a foreign accent.

'Good morning. You're the day nurse, presumably....' He stared yet again. 'What's your name?'

She swallowed, wildly perplexed thoughts racing around in her mind. Why was she so disturbed by the man's voice? He had said little, and yet there seemed to be some meaning behind the prosaic simplicity of the words. She found herself murmuring her name, aware of even more colour rising in her cheeks. He spoke again, repeating her name in a soft and rather gentle tone of voice.

'Tara....' The black eyes seemed to see her discomfiture but the man merely said, 'You can put the tray down, nurse—no, not there. Here, on this smaller table.'

She stiffened, for the table he had indicated was close to where he was standing ... too close!

'I always put it here,' she began, and managed to propel herself towards the larger table. And it was with some surprise that she found herself being allowed to place the tray there, as the whole attitude of the man was one of dominance, of a sort of pagan mastery that convinced her she would have been forced to obey him had he repeated his request for the tray to be put where he had wanted it to be put.

It was as she was straightening up that she heard his voice, low and yet commanding ... and almost sinister.

'Come here.'

She stared, aware of a clamminess in the palms of her hands. She shook her head, staggered at her own lack of resistance. Where was the brisk manner she adopted towards the patients? What had happened to that firm voice she kept especially for the hospital?

'I have to—to go——' Her voice was cut as she saw him gesture with his hand, saw the narrowing of those almost fearsome eyes.

'Come here, Tara.' So soft the voice, but vibrating in a way that made her glance around and even take a step towards the door. Sue had not warned her of this! 'I said, *come here.*' The voice was still very quiet, and Tara did not know what made her move across the floor, obeying his command as if she had been nothing more than an automaton. But suddenly she stopped, forcing herself to resist the strange magnetism with which he seemed to be drawing her to him.

'I said I must go, Mr Petrides. I believe the doctor will be seeing you within the next hour or so.' From what Sue had told her Tara fully expected some protest and found herself waiting for the man to reassert his intention of leaving the hospital. To her surprise he was nodding, obviously fully resigned to waiting for the doctor. 'I shall be back for the tray in about half an hour.'

'I believe,' said the Greek as she turned to leave the ward, 'that I told you to come here.'

Tara spun round, anger flashing in her eyes.

'I don't know what your reason is, Mr Petrides, but your request is one that amazes me. Patients don't usually order the nurses about——' Again her voice was cut, this time by the movement of the man. And she was too late in grasping his intention, too late to escape as he covered the distance between them with the silent smoothness of a jungle cat. She was gripped by the wrists and within seconds she felt the masculine hardness of his body, the warmth of his hand as her face was jerked up, the ruthless possession with which his lips crushed hers. She struggled wildly, using up her strength in vain. The man's strength was incredible, so easily did he hold her, just as if she were not struggling at all. His kiss, fierce and burning, seemed to last for an eternity, and in the end her struggles ceased and she lay passive against him, offering no resistance when with arrogant mastery his mouth forced her lips apart. At last he held her at arms' length, his gaze intently searching her face.

'You surrendered delightfully,' he murmured. 'We shall do very well together——'

'Don't be so ridiculous!' Tara twisted her slender body and managed to release herself from the grip of his hands. 'You—fiend! I shall report this immediately!' She was crimson with anger and embarrassment. For the Greek had been making no false statement when he said she had surrendered. That it was an unwilling surrender, made only when her strength had ebbed to failing point, made no difference. She *had* surrendered, and she knew a terrible deluge of shame and self-disgust. She naturally thought of David, whom she had let down, through no fault of her own. She thought of Sue and wondered why the Greek had not given her a demonstration of his unbridled passion:

'I do not believe you will report that most pleasant little scene, Tara,' the man was saying, his eyes apparently fascinated by her heaving breasts. 'You enjoyed it just as much as I—No,' he said with a commanding gesture of his hand, 'do not deny it. You would have continued to struggle had you felt my kisses to be distasteful——'

'What an inflated opinion you have of your prowess as a lover!' Tara could not have said why she phrased her words like that; she knew only that she was seething with fury and she would have done him a physical injury if that had been at all possible. She looked at the dressing on his forehead and wondered for a moment if the wound had not been so superficial as the doctor believed. Could this injury have affected the man's brain? Tara soon dismissed that idea; the Greek's mental faculties were no more impaired than were her own. He was just a rake whose innate surfeit of ardour had got the better of him! Heaven help his wife, if he had one. She would not only be subjugated mentally but physically as well.

'I have found,' the Greek was saying in response to her angry sarcasm, 'that woman do in fact enjoy my—er—attentions. I am sure that you will admit to enjoying my little demonstration of——'

'You talk like a fool!' she interrupted, glaring at him. 'As for not reporting you—well, that's the first thing I shall do when I leave this room!' And, with far more speed than dignity, she was at the door and, whipping it open, she almost ran through it.

Hateful, *hateful* creature! It was a great pity that the accident had not laid him low—for ever!

She managed to get another nurse to go in for the tray, but did warn her that the man was something of a wolf.

'Made a pass at you, did he?' grinned the nurse. 'One of the hazards of the male ward, of course. If this Greek says a word out of place to me he'll get a swipe over the kisser!'

Naturally Tara was interested to know what had happened when, a few minutes later, the nurse came out with the tray.

'How was he?' she asked, seeing the girl's serene expression.

'Not a word. Very cool and aloof, sort of. Just nodded and picked up a book.'

Tara frowned in puzzlement.

'Strange,' she murmured almost to herself. 'He didn't make a pass at Sue, either.'

'Perhaps he's fallen in love with you at first sight,' laughed the nurse, and went off, leaving Tara scowling ... and wondering why she had changed her mind about reporting the amorous Greek.

That evening she met David and they went to the Royal Oak for dinner. Looking at him across the candlelit table she found herself comparing his handsome open countenance with that of the Greek. And then she frowned, vexed at the way that pagan face kept intruding into her mental vision. David, noticing the frown, enquired the reason for it.

'A hard day at the hospital?' he added, and Tara automatically nodded. 'How was the Greek you mentioned? I hope he didn't speak as arrogantly to you as he spoke to Sue?'

Tara swallowed, wondering what would be David's reaction if she were to relate exactly what happened in that private ward. Guilt swept over her and it made her angry because she was in no way to blame. But yet she could not rid herself of the irksome conviction that she had been untrue to the man she loved. Perhaps, she mused reflectively, she *could* have put up a greater and more prolonged struggle. Perhaps she could even have prevented the Greek from kissing her at all. It seeemed so absurd, in retrospect, that she had been forced into surrender like that. Yes, she should have put up a greater resistance than she had. No wonder she felt guilty. David was speaking, reminding her that she had not answered his question; she looked at him and hoped the light was sufficiently dim for her heightened colour to escape his notice.

'He was rather tiresome,' she returned, thinking that the word was just about the most inadequate she could possibly have used in describing the man's conduct. 'A bad patient; I've told you about them before.'

'Must be very trying on the nerves sometimes.' David took up his knife and fork and cut into his steak. 'Is he still there?'

Tara shook her head.

'He left after lunch.'

'Say goodbye to you?' he asked her with a grin.

'No; nor did I want him to.' She did not add that she had taken good care not to be anywhere around when he departed.

'Good riddance, then! You know, love, I'd feel far happier if you gave up work when we're married.'

'I shall, after a little while,' she returned. 'But for now, David, please bear with me. I do want to have our home furnished, plus all the little extras, before we start a family.'

'I shall bear with you, darling,' he smiled. 'Yours is a most excellent idea, as we're both agreed that once the children arrive their mother shouldn't go out to work.'

The following morning Tara was handed a magnificent bouquet of roses by the porter, who said how lucky she was.

'They're not for me,' she was saying even as he was handing them to her. 'You've made a mistake. Aren't they beautiful! Some lucky patient is well and truly held in affection. Let me have a look at the card.' She was holding the bouquet, two dozen or more long-stemmed roses delightfully arranged in their cellophane wrapping, with a wide bow of silver ribbon to tie them together.

'They *are* for you,' the porter said, eyeing her with a new interest. 'From an admirer by the name of Leonides.'

Leonides.... Tara felt herself go taut. It must be the Greek! How dare he! She glared angrily at the card, scarcely able to contain herself, and prevented from tearing it to shreds only by the awareness of the porter, standing there waiting for her reaction.

'Thank you, Bill,' she said, hoping she sounded as casual as she intended to. 'A grateful patient. I do wish they wouldn't waste their money in this way.' She gave a shrug of her shoulders. 'They mean well, of course.'

'Of course,' agreed Bill in an expressionless tone.

'Nice flowers, though. Must have cost a small fortune!'

Tara, her temper boiling up inside her, could almost have thrown the flowers away. Almost, but of course she did no such thing. They were so beautiful that she could not resist taking some considerable time in arranging them in a large bowl, using, with them, some pretty green foliage which she brought in from the hospital garden. Everyone wanted to know who the roses were for, and who had sent them. Tara, hating to lie but unable to do anything else because she had no intention of saying they were hers, sent to her by the Greek whom all the staff had heard of since Sue had broadcast to all and sundry what he had been like, said she had received them from the porter and the card seemed to have got lost. It had in fact been put into one of the dustbins.

Later, Tara was called to the telephone, Leonides Petrides speaking, she heard. Did she like the roses? She replaced the receiver instantly but found herself trembling. What should she do? She did toy with the idea of confiding in David but, somehow, she was afraid to do so. She ought not to be afraid, since her fiancé was naturally the one to whom she should turn in any emergency or other occasion when she needed help or advice.

She decided to ignore the Greek's conduct, assuming he would soon become tired of these absurdities. But that evening as she left her flat in the nurses' new building she came face to face with him before she was half way to the nearby bus stop.

'Go away!' she cried before he could speak. 'If you keep molesting me I shall ask for police protection!'

'No such thing.' He gestured towards a car standing by the kerb. 'Get in and we'll talk. I shall not take no for an answer, Tara,' he added imperiously when she attempted to interrupt. 'We have to talk, understand? Our paths have crossed; we cannot just fade out of each other's lives. Please get into my car and——'

'Do you suppose for one moment I'm that kind of a fool!' She made to dodge past him, but he barred her way. She glanced around, troubled that she might be seen from one of the many windows of the nurses' quarters. 'Why you should think we have anything to talk about I can't imagine. Kindly let me pass; I have a bus to catch!'

'Where are you going?' His voice with its slight foreign accent was low, but the arrogance was clear. 'I can give you a lift.'

'I'm going to meet my fiancé!' she flared. 'So please get out of my way!'

'Your——!' He stared down into her lovely face, a face framed by a halo of golden hair, long and straight but flicked up at the ends in a sort of enchanting disarray. A half-fringe adorned her high, intelligent forehead, curling round towards her temple. 'Your ... fiancé?' His voice sounded hollow, and Tara, perplexed by his changed manner, stared interrogatingly at him, her anger for the moment set aside. 'You are engaged to be married?'

'Yes, I am.' Her answer was brief; she felt oddly disturbed, as when a pain is inadvertently inflicted on someone. 'And now, Mr Petrides, will you please allow me to pass you? My bus will be here at any moment— It's here now,' she added urgently as out of the corner of her eye she saw it through the trees. 'I must go——'

'No!' Imperious the voice, and the pagan face was taut—even cruel in its expression. 'I'll give you a lift.'

She tried to pass him but in the end gave up, furious with him and yet at the same time aware that the feeling of concern was still with her.

'I've missed it!' She felt like crying, and that was not surprising, she thought, considering the way this foreigner was persecuting her. 'My—my fiancé'll be worried about m-me. Oh, why are you pestering me like this!'

'Haven't you guessed?' he enquired softly.

'Guessed?' She shook her head, scarcely able to concentrate as her thoughts were entirely with David, waiting there, with his car, for her to alight from the bus and get in beside him. He would have come for her each evening but they had more time together if she caught the bus and met him in town. 'Guessed what?'

'Never mind. Get into my car and I'll take you to your fiancé.' He sounded sincere and, strangely, Tara trusted him to keep his word.

'Very well.' She hated his touch as he put a hand beneath her elbow, helping her into his car. She sat there stiffly upright, wondering if she ought to have trusted him after the way he had first treated her.

'I want to talk to you, Tara,' he said after a while. 'Is there any real hurry for you to meet this fiancé of yours?'

'He'll be waiting for me at the bus stop.'

'Then we have a few minutes, as we can always overtake the bus.' And without waiting for her response he swung off the main road and into a tree-lined country lane. Dusk was falling, as it was the beginning of April; Tara felt her heart give a great lurch, but knew that her protestations would fall on deaf ears. Leonides Petrides pulled up on a grass verge. 'You can't marry this fiancé you're going to meet,' he told her without preamble. 'You and he are not meant for one another.'

'What are you talking about?' she demanded wrathfully. 'You've never met my fiancé——' She broke off, sighing helplessly. 'You must be quite mad,' she declared. 'I ought to have asked for police protection in the first place!'

He looked at her in mild surprise.

'What have I done?' he wanted to know.

'Kissed me, and sent me flowers, and telephoned

me! And now you've forced me into your car. . . .' Her
voice trailed off to silence as she saw the expression of
amusement that came into his eyes.

'Do you suppose you'll be given police protection for
such things as those? I did not force you into the car,
you know, Tara. You came willingly. I shall keep my
promise and deliver you up to your fiancé, but not until
you and I have talked. If you persist in voicing these
angry allegations against me we shall get nowhere, so
I advise you—if you really wish to meet your fiancé this
evening—to adopt a more conciliatory manner and
give us the opportunity of discussing my proposition.'

'Your—proposition, Mr Petrides?'

'Leonides is the name,' he told her calmly. 'You
would have noticed it on the card I sent with the roses.'
He was sitting sideways in his seat, looking at her profile. 'My friends call me Leon.'

'Well, as I'm not your friend, or likely to be, I'll call
you Mr Petrides, and you will oblige me by calling me
Miss Bennet. This proposition,' she went on. 'If you
must put it to me, then please do so at once, and then
take me to my fiancé.' Although she spoke calmly her
heart was beating far too quickly. She felt she was in
some strange realm of the unknown, waiting, as if in
limbo, for something dramatic to happen.

And something dramatic did happen. The Greek
calmly asked her to marry him.

Tara, recalling this moment afterwards, when her
mind was cleared of the fog that enveloped it on the
instant of his incredible offer of marriage, could never
understand why she just sat there, staring at him, instead of opening the car door and making her escape.
It was as if he were exerting his influence upon her,
using his magnetism to keep her at his side until he had
said everything he wanted to say. And this was that he
could give her a good life, that she would live in a
beautiful white and blue villa on the delightful island

of Hydra in Greece, that she would have servants, and an allowance which would be more than adequate for her needs, even though they might with time become extravagant. She made no attempt to stop his flow of words but marvelled at the ease with which he spoke of things which to her seemed so unreal as to be meaningless. She must be in a trance, or dreaming. This fantastic situation could not happen in real life.

'You are not saying anything, Tara,' he said when, after pausing for a while, he had invited some sort of response from her. She looked at him in profile, noting the dark skin, clear and shining, the aquiline nose, the jutting chin. A man who would have his own way, who could coerce most people into bending to his will. She spoke hurriedly, as if she just had to show him that he had no power over her at all.

'I'm going to be married in eight days, Mr Petrides——'

'Eight days!' The black eyes glittered as he turned to face her and she put a hand instinctively to her throat, fear rising within her. This man desired her, no mistake about that. His desire carried him to the extent of offering her marriage, which, she felt sure, had never been offered to any other of the women he had admitted associating with. He looked ready to murder her fiancé, she thought, as he went on to say, 'You will not marry anyone in eight days—unless it is me!'

Sheer terror took possession of Tara, spurring her into action. She was out of the car before he could prevent her and she did not stop running until she had reached the main road. He took some time in turning the car round in the narrow lane, so that when he eventually emerged from it on to the wider road, Tara had disappeared into a wood, where she crouched down out of sight until she saw his car go speeding past in the direction taken by the bus.

# CHAPTER TWO

THE white bridal gown was a model of perfection. Sue, Tara's chief bridesmaid, stood back after Tara was dressed and gave a gasp of appreciation.

'You look beautiful! I've never seen you look so lovely!'

Tara, though blushing under this flattery, was happy that she was looking so perfect for the man she loved. He would be waiting to claim her as his own, his wife, for ever.

'Oh, but I've never been so happy!' She looked in the mirror and sighed. 'In an hour—perhaps an hour and a quarter—I shall be Mrs David Rothwell.' She cut the last word rather abruptly, tensed and frightened suddenly. For a very dark face appeared before her, and in her ears the name Leon Petrides seemed to be ringing. *Mrs* Leon Petrides.... This could have been her name had she chosen.

'Tara, what's wrong, for heaven's sake?' Sue's voice, sharp-edged with concern, mercifully took the ringing from her ears. 'You looked almost—desolate!' Sue shook her head, as if trying to negate what she had just said. 'I mean, you looked unhappy—somehow.'

'What a thing to say!' Tara's voice sounded cracked even to her own ears. 'I'm the happiest girl alive!' But she was again thinking of the Greek, who had sought her out on the third evening after that escape she had made. She had been out with David; he had brought her home and dropped her at the entrance to the nurses' block of flats. Tara had stood on the step to wave to him, and she made no move until the car had disappeared. And then, before she had even time to cry out, she was caught in the Greek's arms and for the second time forced to endure his kisses.

Endure...: She blushed hotly even now as she recalled her confusion of mind, her failure to call for help even though, after the first spate of his passion had passed, Leonides Petrides had held her from him, scanning her face in the dim light from the electric bulb overhead. He had laughed softly, in triumph, and guided her unresistingly to the shadows of the hospital gardens. There he had pulled her again to his hard body, had pressed his demanding mouth to hers, conquering her sudden spurt of resistance by taking one firm breast in his hand and caressing it in a way that was both tender and yet possessive. She struggled mentally but surrendered physically, surrendered as she had never even thought of doing with David.

But then David had never tempted her in the way the experienced Greek had tempted her. A woman would have to be made of stone before she could resist him ... and Tara was by no means made of stone. She learned things about herself which she had never known existed; she experienced sensations of sheer ecstasy, allowing herself to be carried on the tide of his unbridled pagan ardour. His lovemaking was subtle, so characterised by finesse that every nerve in her body was affected, every desire awakened until she almost craved for the final act of fulfilment. Nothing mattered except that she was in his arms; David was a nebulous figure simply because she had no room in her mind or heart for anyone or anything in these moments of total bliss. Leon Petrides ordered her to say his name and she obeyed at once. He told her that fate had meant them for one another and she agreed. He commanded her to break off her engagement and she said she would do as he told her. She was as putty in his hands, a mortal in the power of a pagan Greek god. The moon had come from behind the clouds to highlight her face and she had again heard his low laugh of triumph.

'I'm your master,' he had whispered. 'I own you, body and soul. You'll come to me, be my wife, and we shall be happy for ever. You will be enchanted with my island, Tara; it has no roads so no traffic. Hills and valleys, the calm blue sea all around you when you stand on the patio and gaze one way and another. Flowers for your hair, jewels for your throat.' His lips came down, gently taking hers. She gave her own lips freely, gladly; she embraced him as he embraced her. And when at last she begged him to let her go, she had made the solemn promise that she would be his wife.

But with the daylight, and the stark reality of a hospital ward, sanity had swiftly returned. A deluge of shame swept over her and she wanted to cry out for forgiveness. She had lost for ever the innocence that had always charmed her fiancé; she was no longer a shy and inexperienced little girl whom David liked to call his 'darling babe'.

She had drunk the heady wine of pagan love, but yet she knew a deep and bitter hatred for the Greek. Why had he come into her life at all? He had talked of fate, and Tara cursed fate for throwing him in her path. Her life had been smooth, her love affair gentle, perhaps a little unexciting, but it was satisfying in that comradeship went hand in hand with the physical pleasure they had derived from their tender lovemaking. With the Greek there was an inferno of passion, a storm of unrestraint that brought wild ecstatic pulsations to the heart, sweeping all before it, robbing the mind of all except the bliss of the moment.

Tara had cut the Greek out of her mind, had made sure that he could never molest her again, by asking David to call for her each evening, and when later on he brought her home she immediately ran into the building and to her own little flat. Leon had made her arrange a meeting with him at an hotel in town; she did not of course keep the appointment. He had several times ·rung her up at the hospital, but she told the operator not to put the calls through to her.

'Tell him I'm busy, or off work—anything! He's making a nuisance of himself!'

And so her wedding day had been reached without any further meeting and at last Tara felt safe. As she had just remarked to Sue, in an hour and a quarter at the most she would be David's wife.

'The taxi's here, Tara.' Sue's voice cut into her thoughts and she took the bouquet of pink and white carnations from the chair where Sue had placed it on its arrival. The brother of a friend was giving Tara away and he was smiling as she got into the taxi beside him.

'Gosh, you look gorgeous!' Jake exclaimed. 'What a lucky man David is! Why didn't I get in first?' He was joking, of course, and Tara joined in his laughter. She was happy, having put Leon from her mind, disciplining it to thoughts of her lovely day and the honeymoon to follow after the reception at the Golden Lion where a buffet meal had been arranged. The taxi seemed to be travelling rather slowly, Tara noticed after a while, and she remarked on this to her companion.

'Yes,' he agreed. 'The driver did mention when he picked·me up that there was something wrong with the works, as he put it. I think it'll get us there on time, though,' he added, glancing at his watch.

But just when the taxi was travelling along a lonely stretch of road it seemed to give several jerks and finally came to a stop. Jake was frowning, Tara looking troubled as the driver came to the door and opened it.

'Sorry, but it's just stopped on me. I'll take a look under the bonnet.'

Tara looked intently at the man, puzzled by his accent. His English was excellent, but not quite perfect. His hair and eyes were dark, his skin bronzed. What nationality was he? So many foreigners worked in

Britain these days that one could not always make a correct guess at the countries from which they originated.

'Don't be alarmed,' said Jake soothingly as he noticed her expression. 'If he can't get it going in a moment or two he'll have another taxi here in no time at all.'

And he did.

Tara, whose only concern was to get to the church in good time, needed no encouragement to hurry from one taxi to the other. The driver, obviously aware of the urgency, stayed in his seat, leaving it to the other driver to open the door for Tara. She got in, expecting to see Jake enter from the other side. But without warning she was given a little push that sent her sprawling on to the seat; the door was slammed and the car shot away, instantly gathering speed. Dazed for a moment, Tara could scarcely grasp what had happened, the only thought in her head being that there was another delay, as the man would have to stop and then go back for Jake.

'You've forgotten the gentleman——'

'Sit back and relax, Tara,' drawled a voice that instantly set her heart pounding so violently that she felt physically sick. 'We've a long way to go——'

'Let me out of here!' she cried, unconsciously hammering on the back of his seat. 'Stop—immediately!'

Leon Petrides took off the cap he was wearing and tossed it carelessly on to the seat beside him. Tara saw him brush a hand through his hair as though he were relieved to be free of the cap.

'I said, sit back and relax.' The accented voice was imperious in spite of its softness. 'I shall be driving at speed, so I advise you not to open the door.'

'I *shall* open it!' She glanced through the window; the car was travelling at sixty miles an hour at least. 'I'll open the window and scream,' she amended, her brain working frantically to find a way out of this terrifying situation. Fool that she had been, sublimely tak-

ing it for granted that she had outwitted the Greek. But
never could she have visualised, even in her wildest
flights of fancy, his going to lengths as dramatic and
daring as these. 'You can't possibly get away with this!'
she cried. 'The police will already have been alerted;
your accomplice will have been arrested——'

'My dear,' interrupted Leon Petrides quietly, 'you
are merely voicing your hopes. The man who helped
me was an employee of mine whom I sent for a few days
ago when, realising you had every intention of breaking the promise you made to me, I decided to abduct
you and take you to my home in Greece. He will have
driven off immediately, before your friend could gather
his wits sufficiently to guess that it was a plot. This employee will be on my boat when we arrive at Bridport——'

'Boat?' she broke in hollowly. 'You're—you're taking
me to a b-boat?' She looked down at the lovely bouquet
she held, and the tears could no longer be suppressed.
'Please let me go,' she cried. 'I don't kn-know what
you're expecting to gain by running off with me!
You'll be caught, and sent to jail. Surely you're afraid?'

'Do I look like a man who's afraid?' he asked with a
trace of amusement. And then, ignoring the rest of
what she had said, 'You ask me what I shall gain. A
wife, Tara, the girl who promised to marry me and
then went back on her word.' So soft the voice, and
smoothly even, but beneath it all there was anger, fierce
and terrifyingly primitive. Tara shivered, aware that
her whole body was cold.

'I shall never marry you!' she cried. 'Never! I'm
marrying David and nothing's going to stop me!' She
spoke wildly, urged by fear. This foreigner was so cool
and confident. That he was committing a felony seemed
not to affect him in the least. 'You're mad!' she went
on, frustrated that he would not speak. 'You can't take
me to Greece against my will! How can you possibly

get me there?' she added, trying to affect a confidence she was far from feeling. 'There's no way——'

'I've said we're going by boat,' he broke in to remind her, his lean brown hand lifted to smother a yawn. 'I am hoping that, once aboard, you will become re-signed and behave yourself. However, if you do not behave I shall have you locked in your cabin and not allowed out until the end of the voyage.' He increased his speed to over eighty miles an hour. 'Fate has thrown us together; we must not fight our destiny, Tara, for it was mapped out before our birth.'

'You talk like a fool!'

'And you talk unguardedly,' he warned. 'I am not used to being spoken to with disrespect. You must learn, and quickly, if you want to avoid punishment.'

She gritted her teeth, fury erasing—for the moment —all her terror.

'If you think for one moment I shall treat you with respect then you are a fool—an idiot, in fact! Who would respect a criminal—an abductor?'

'My wife will respect me,' he stated softly, 'just as all others with whom I come into contact respect me.'

'Just who are you?' she demanded curiously.

'Your husband ... and your master.'

She could have struck him if the action would not have endangered her life. There must be a way out of this, she thought frantically—and then her heart leapt as the solution occurred to her.

'My passport!' she cried triumphantly. 'You won't be able to take me far without that....' Her voice trailed and her eyes dilated, for while she was speaking he was bringing something from his pocket, and now he held it up before her incredulous eyes. 'You ... stole it ... but how——?'

'My man—the taxi-driver. He burgled your rooms. It was simple, so he tells me.' Leon replaced the passport and concentrated on his driving. The trees flew past as he headed for the coast and the picturesque little resort of Bridport.... And there he had a boat. But she would escape somehow, for how could he possibly force her aboard with people about?

# CHAPTER THREE

IT was dark when they reached the harbour. Tara scarcely had time to glance around before a hand was clapped over her mouth and she was hustled into a motor boat and taken aboard the motor yacht. It seemed to have happened in a flash, so that all she had rehearsed on the final, silent miles of the car journey faded into nothingness and she was being pushed un-ceremoniously into a teak-panelled cabin from where she could hear the rhythmic throb of engines already running. The boat had seven berths plus crew, she had been told by her abductor, and an owner's cabin which was fitted out with almost everything one would find in a top class hotel. She was not in this grand cabin, but there was a fitted wardrobe with a pretty vanitory unit attached to one side. The bed was soft to her touch, and covered with a blue lace counterpane over a white blanket. Tara sat down on it, tears streaming down her face as she thought of what might have been but for the criminal act of this Greek savage who had her in his power. She would have been married, a happy glowing bride travelling to the honeymoon hotel—— She cut her thoughts as a renewed flood of tears escaped. But inevitably her mind was soon dwelling on the same thoughts again. She wondered what had transpired as a result of her disappearance. Obviously Jake's first act would be to reach the nearest phone and contact the police. But they had not found her and now—now, she told herself—they never would. How could they? There was no reason for them to connect her abductor with the owner of the *Catana*, luxury crusier moored at a little Dorset harbour. Tara's thoughts wandered to the first time she had been alone with Leonides Petrides, and she deplored her own behaviour in not telling David about him. She had told no one at all, so his name could not in any way be brought up when the police were conducting their interviews with the various people who knew her. Fool that she had been! Looking back it seemed only logical to complain about the Greek's molestations, and yet she had kept silent.

She turned as she heard the cabin door open. Leon stood in the doorway, one hand resting idly on the jamb and the other thrust into his pocket. On his teak-brown face a sardonic smile played, reflected in his pitchblende eyes. She found herself noticing the dignity of his pose, the arrogance of his features—patrician, Greek and pagan. The dark eyes moved, slowly, insolently, over her white-clad figure and his amusement seemed to increase.

'Pity we haven't a priest on board,' he commented mockingly as he advanced into the cabin. 'He could have married us, seeing that you are already attired for the occasion.'

She was almost in tears again; she did not know whether to threaten or to plead, but looking up into his granite-hard, implacable countenance she felt with sinking heart that nothing she could do or say would have the slightest effect on him.

'What—what are your in-intentions?' she managed to whisper at last, and she saw the mocking expression that entered his eyes.

'What an absurd question to ask, my dear. You know what my intentions are——' He broke off and laughed to himself, then fell into a reflective mood before he continued, 'For the first time in my life my intentions are honourable. I intend to marry you.' The black eyes flickered over her slender, drooping figure, staying for a moment on her hands, which were twisting and un-twisting all the time, a release for the fear and uncertainty that dwelt within her. 'You should be flattered, and happy—not looking as downcast as if some great tragedy were affecting you.' The alien voice had taken on an edge of sternness, and the thin nostrils moved slightly, as if anger affected their owner. 'Shall I command you to smile or are you going to do it voluntarily?'

The ready tears rolled down her white cheeks.

'Let me go,' she begged. 'Take me back—please, oh, *please*! Won't you take me back, if I promise—promise not to give you away to—the—p-police?'

'Would I have gone to all this trouble if I were going to allow myself to be persuaded to take you back?'

'You're heartless!' she cried, wringing her hands, then stretching them out in a gesture of humble pleading. 'I was to be married—I'd—I'd be married to David n-now and going on—on my honeymoon. Be—be kind to me and let me go—go to the man I love!'

He stood erect, unmoved by her anguished entreaties. The black eyes were alight, fiercely holding hers, merciless in the intensity of their stare. She remembered how he had held her eyes to his before, as if he would hypnotise her, bending her to his will.

'You think you love that man, but I assure you that you don't, and marriage to him would have proved disastrous. I have saved you and one day you'll thank me.'

'I'll never thank you!' she cried in a choking voice. 'What right have you, a foreigner, to feel you've the right to interfere in my life?'

'I shall not only interfere in your life,' he stated calmly, 'but I shall, from now on, control it.'

She gasped at the sheer arrogant pomposity of his statement, and the manner of its delivery. If he were a god he could not assume any greater dictatorship than this! Anger rose within her, transcending everything else—fear, distress and hopelessness.

'Get out of here and leave me alone!' she almost shouted. 'Get out, and stay out!'

For answer he laughed lightly and reached for her hand.

'You have spirit,' he observed, 'and I like a woman with spirit, which is why I prefer an English wife to a Greek one. They've been brought up to be meek——' His grip tightened painfully on her wrist as she tried to snatch it from his hold. 'However,' he continued languidly, 'do not think, Tara, that I will allow my wife too much liberty where her behaviour and her tongue are concerned. The Greek male is traditionally master in his own house, and I am Greek.' He looked at her, frowning suddenly at the evidence of tears on her face. 'I hope I make myself clear?'

She looked at him, white to the lips but strangely composed now, for she felt that dignity might impress him more effectively than anger.

'Perfectly clear. But as I'm not your wife the traditions of the Greeks can't affect me.'

Again he laughed, and pulled her slender frame towards him. She found herself against his hard body, seethed when her chin was tilted so that she was forced to look into his eyes. His lips came down, slowly, as if he savoured the revulsion that came to her face. His words told her she was right.

'You can look like that now—as if you hate me—but in a moment or two you'll be thrilled by my kisses——'

'Thrilled!' she almost spat out at him, her eyes blazing. 'What an opinion you have of yourself!'

'My experience with you,' he reminded her tauntingly, 'was more than enough for me to realise that you'd make a reciprocative bed-mate——'

'Stop it!' Again she broke into what he was saying, her resolve to be dignified forgotten in the swell of anger that consumed her, anger born mainly from the knowledge—the hateful, reluctant admission—that he

was speaking the truth when he implied that she had
enjoyed his passionate lovemaking. 'Let me go—you
might as well, because I shall never be your wife,
never!'

'Then you shall be my pillow-friend,' was his calm
rejoinder. 'I mean to have you, Tara, so it will be
more comfortable if you resign yourself to the inevitable.' And with that his arms encircled her in a hawser-
like embrace and his lips thrust against hers, bruising
them, mastering her attempts to keep them closed. The
ardour of his actions was resisted for a while, but it
became too much for her—the sensual movements of
his lean lithe body against hers, the pagan mastery of
his lips, the possessive arrogance of his caressing
hands. . . . He took her breast, gently, the movements
of his fingers a persuasion that was irresistible, and she
found herself pressing against him, as she had before,
especially on the night she had promised to marry him.
Shaken when at last he released her, she stood there,
limp and weeping, bewildered and lost, unable to
think clearly or even to speak to him. His eyes were
fixed on her face; one hand picked up a few folds of
her wedding-dress.

'Yes,' he nodded with a little sigh which she felt was
an affectation, 'it's a great pity we haven't a priest on
board.'

'I can't see that it would make any difference,' she
flashed. 'I'd refuse to marry you.'

'A refusal that would not do you much good, my
dear.'

She looked at him; he had let the dress fall and the
folds he had held mingled with the others. She was able
to move away unhindered.

'The priest would have to be as big a villain as you,'
she said, watching his expression with interest.

'I have friends,' he told her mildly. 'We shall be married, I assure you.'

'I'm to be forced to the altar?' Her eyes never wavered from his face, but as before she read nothing from the fixed unsmiling stare he gave her. 'At gunpoint, perhaps?'

He gave a short laugh.

'Nothing quite as melodramatic as that,' he assured her.

'What kind of coercion are you intending to use?' She was asking the question automatically, her mind elsewhere as she tried to capture a picture of what was happening at home. David heartbroken—and his parents who had come to love her; his sister Mary with whom she got on so well. The concern and confusion that must have occurred in the church when the bride failed to appear on time, and then Jake appearing with his dramatic and incredible news that she had been kidnapped. Again Tara cursed herself for not telling someone about the Greek who had kept on pestering her.

'If you refuse the honourable state of marriage,' he was replying suavely, 'then you will be my pillow-friend. I've already told you so.' She made no answer because an idea had come to her; it was clutching at a straw, she knew, but it might bring results. 'I believe, though,' the Greek was adding, 'that you will choose marriage, since you are the kind of girl who would shrink from what you considered to be dishonourable.'

'I intend to be neither your wife nor your mistress!'

'Brave words,' he applauded with mocking amusement, 'but ineffectual under the circumstances. I have you in my power and you know it.' The dark foreign eyes swept her figure, stripping it naked. 'I can take you now, this very moment, if I choose.'

She coloured at his words and under the roving, all-seeing glance, and for a space she hesitated before speaking what was in her mind. Would it work? Well, she would soon find out. She looked him in the eye and said,

'Do you really believe you can get away with this abduction? Do you suppose I haven't talked to anyone about the way you made a nuisance of yourself?' She managed to laugh and hoped it sounded convincing. 'I've told several people! My fiancé knows about you—and some of the nurses at the hospital! I've told so many people! The police have only to put a few questions here and there to get all the clues they need! You'll be arrested the moment we land in Greece—and you'll stand trial and be sent to prison for years and years. . . .' Her voice began to falter to a lower pitch as she noticed the expression of sheer amusement that had settled on his face. Her words petered out altogether as a low laugh tilted the corners of his mouth. She swallowed convulsively; she should have known the hateful man would see through her deceit.

'My child,' he said with some considerable humour, 'how transparent you are! You've thought of all this only seconds ago.'

'It's the truth!' she said persistently, fighting to the very last inch. 'True, I tell you! You'll regret it if you ignore my warning!'

'It's a good try,' he said, regarding her imperturbably from his superior height. 'But you seem to have forgotten that you were willing, just now, to promise not to give me away to the police. Such a promise would be of little use if the police were already on the scent. And that is not the only blunder you've made. If you'd been so sure of rescue, and of my early arrest, you would not have pleaded the way you have.' His eyes became admiring. 'You're not the girl to plead in that craven way——'

'I was *not* craven!' She looked as if she could have murdered him for using a word like that.

'See what I mean? You have spirit, and I know just

what it cost you to beg like that. You'd never have done it if, in your secret mind, you knew you would soon be rescued by the forces of the law.'

'I hate you,' she quivered. 'I'd kill you if I could!'

'At this moment, perhaps,' he agreed unconcernedly. 'But later you will feel very differently. I can so easily make you.'

Her teeth clenching, she turned away and he went out, only to return a few minutes later carrying three cardboard boxes which he placed on the bed.

'You'd better change,' he recommended. 'You can't go about in a wedding-dress all the time.' He paused, a mocking smile curving his mouth at her expression. 'Yes, I have bought you clothes,' he told her. 'Top ones which I hope will meet your approval and underwear which I know will meet with mine, seeing that I chose them.'

She stared, revolted.

'You went into a shop for—for underwear?'

He laughed and assured her that he was used to buying such things.

'My various pillow-friends have always expected this kind of gift—among more expensive ones, of course.'

The contempt in her eyes grew, a circumstance which at last appeared to anger him. His mouth tightened, but as yet that was the only outward sign of his feelings.

'You've had numerous women, evidently.'

He inclined his head.

'A fair number,' he agreed, his glance straying to the bed. 'Aren't you going to open the boxes?'

'No, I am not!'

The compression of his mouth became more pronounced. He flicked a hand imperiously.

'Open the boxes,' he commanded.

'I shan't,' she returned defiantly. 'I don't want your

gifts, as you call them! Take them to some other of
your friends!'

His eyes narrowed threateningly.

'Obey me,' he said harshly. 'If you knew me better
you wouldn't need a second telling.'

'Ordering, you mean!'

'I'm in no mood for inane arguments, Tara! Do as
I say, at once!'

She shook her head, a little afraid now on account of
his manner which was threatening to say the least.

'I don't want your presents,' she began, then gave a
little squeal of pain as her wrist was taken in a vicious
grip.

'Do as I tell you!' he thundered. 'I shall make you, so
you might as well capitulate before you receive something that will both hurt and humiliate.' There was no
mistaking the significant inflection in his voice and
after a mere moment's pause Tara walked stiffly to the
bed and, after undoing the string, which was in a bow,
she lifted the lid of one of the boxes. 'Take it out,'
ordered her captor authoritatively. 'You'll be delighted
with it!'

She did as she was told, extracting the diaphanous
nightgown from its wrappings of tissue paper.

She flung it on the bed and turned, tears in her eyes.

'Let me go,' she pleaded in a small voice. 'I haven't
done you any harm, so please let me go.' Even before
she had stopped speaking he was shaking his head, and
a spasm of sheer hopelessness swept through her. She
put her hands to her face, but before she had time to
weep into them they were removed and she was taken
almost gently into Leon's arms.

'Don't take it to heart, my child,' he said. 'It seems
much worse than it is, I assure you. At present you can
think only of the wedding you missed and the man
you would have married. But it will all soon fade when
we are man and wife; you'll know that it is I who is

meant to be your husband and lover.' He tilted her chin and tapped her cheek possessively. 'Now, cheer up. Nothing irritates me more than a weeping woman. Undo another box—— No, there are other things in that one. Take them out first.'

Tara looked at him and knew it was wise to obey him. She withdrew bras and panties, another nightgown and a lacy petticoat. He ordered her to open another box, and then the last one. She put everything on the bed—two dresses and two skirts, three blouses and several items of clothing for use on a beach—or the deck of a pleasure boat. Everything bore labels of one of the most expensive fashion houses in Paris. Raising her eyes to his face, Tara said,

'You're a wealthy man, obviously.'

'I have enough,' he answered carelessly.

'More than enough for your own good!' she flashed at him, and again saw his eyes narrow threateningly.

'Be careful,' he warned in a very soft voice. 'You've seen only the best side of me——'

'The best!' she exclaimed, and a laugh broke from her lips. 'My God, if this is your best side then I hope I never see any other!'

He advanced towards her and she stepped back until her calves touched the bed.

'You ask for it, my girl! Shall I make you smart—or shall I bring you to heel in a very different way?' Without giving her time to answer he brought her to him with a savage jerk and, thrusting her head back, he pressed his lips to hers. She struggled even while aware that it was hopeless. His hands roved, caressing, but by no means gently this time. His mouth was cruel in its demands, his body movements erotically persuasive. Tara fought both physically and mentally, but all her efforts met with failure within minutes. He was too masterful for her, too arrogantly confident and determined; he would force her surrender, he whispered, his lips caressing her ear. She tried to push him away, but her hands were imprisoned behind her back for a while before, with a quiet but authoritative inflection, Leon told her to put her arms around his neck. She obeyed, and when he told her to kiss him she obeyed again. He laughed and she hated the sound. He held her from him and she detested the triumph that lit his eyes, mingling with the humour already there.

Her temper surged and without considering the consequences she bit the finger that was caressing her mouth. He winced, his body caught in a spasm of pain. She saw his disbelieving stare and tried to escape. But it was too late and she felt that hell had been let loose within him as, catching hold of a handful of her hair, he dragged her head back with a ruthlessness that brought a cry of pain to her lips.

'You ... wretch! I ought to pay you in your own medicine!' Instead, his hands touched her throat, then encased it, closing slowly, increasing the pressure. Her eyes dilated and the fear he saw appeared to satisfy him. His hands were withdrawn from her neck. 'Just a warning,' he told her softly, 'in case you should ever be that foolish again.'

'I hate you,' she whispered, every vestige of colour having left her face. 'I'll kill you if ever I get the opportunity!'

He moved away, flicking a hand negligently.

'Try one of the dresses on for size,' he ordered, and sat down on the stool by the dressing-table.

'If I must,' she said huskily, 'then please let me do it in private.'

'Why the fuss? We shall be married in a few days' time.'

'No!' She shook her head in violent protest. 'You can't make me! No priest is going to take the risk!'

'We shall be married in a few days' time,' he re-.

peated, flicking a hand again. 'The blue one—let me see it on you.'

She stood unmoving, bitter hatred in her eyes.

'What satisfaction can it do you to order me about like this? You've taken me from my fiancé, ruined my life——' Breaking off on a little sob, she burst into tears. 'I wish I were dead!' she cried. 'Let me go—you can't want a woman whose hatred is such that she'd like to see you lying dead at her feet!'

'I've said you'll not always feel like this.' He stretched a long leg in front of him, making himself as comfortable as was possible, sitting on the stool as he was. 'Stop dwelling on the past and look to the future.'

She turned her back on him, lifting her dress as she walked.

'There is no future for me,' she whispered hopelessly. 'I can't see any light in my life if you keep me prisoner.'

He got to his feet.

'I'll be back in five minutes,' he said. 'I shall expect to see you in the blue dress.'

She watched him depart, closing the door and locking it after him. Voices were heard a moment later and she supposed he was giving orders to the crew, as the boat began to move and, looking through the porthole, she saw the lights of the hotels retreating. The boat was pulling away from the harbour, so all formalities must have been gone through. Her heart seemed to stop beating for a few bleak and hopeless seconds. How could she escape? One day, perhaps, but before then much could happen. She began to cry again, then stopped, her mouth tightening. Tears would not get her very far, but resolve might—resolve to fight him in any way that presented itself. He might in the end rue the day he had abducted her!

She took off her wedding dress and laid it down across the end of the bed. How different her feelings when, a few hours ago, she had stepped into it and Sue had zipped her up! Life had been good—roses and red wine all the way! It seemed impossible that she was here, on the foreigner's boat, his prisoner, while her fiancé was frantic, wondering what could have happened to her. He would be pestering the police, would be blaming Jake, perhaps, for not taking more care of her. All the guests. . . . It did not bear thinking about and Tara tried to fix her mind on thoughts of escape, which would be far more profitable.

She was wearing the dress when Leon returned. His eyes wandered, taking in every curve and line of her figure. He nodded his approval.

'Very attractive. The colour suits you; it matches your eyes. Put the wedding dress away,' he commanded abruptly as he saw it lying there across the bed. 'You can throw it overboard,' he added as the idea came to him.

'Throw it overboard?' Tara shook her head, her eyes filling up. 'I shall do no such thing!'

'Then I will.' He strode purposefully across the cabin and, picking up the lovely flowing gown, he bundled it into one of the cardboard boxes and put on the lid. With it under his arm he went to the door. 'I expect you're hungry,' he observed. 'We'll have dinner in the saloon, but in case you have any ideas of making a fuss I'll tell you that my crew—who are all Greeks—have instructions to ignore any pleas you might make to them. And if you think there is any way of escape, then I must disillusion you here and now.'

'There is one way,' returned Tara challengingly, looking straight at him, 'and that's overboard!'

'I should bring you out,' was Leon's cool rejoinder, and he added that she would regret a move like that because he would soundly box her ears.

'One of the crew will come and tell you when the meal is ready to be served——' He glanced at his watch.

'Should be in about ten minutes or so. His name is Carlos; he'll show you where to come.'

'I shan't be having anything to eat——'

'You'll do as you're told,' he interrupted imperiously, then left her, locking the door again after him.

# CHAPTER FOUR

TARA looked at herself in the mirror, wanted to burst into tears again but managed to control the impulse. She and David would have been dining together, and after that. . . .

It was a deep sigh rather than a sob that broke from her lips; she thought about her captor, and about her statement that she would like to see him dead. Would it be possible to maim him? she wondered, amazed at the cold and practical way she was considering this. If he could be put out of action then surely she would be able to escape.

A knock on the cabin door was followed by the sound of a key being turned. A stocky, swarthy-skinned Greek stood by in the opening, a grin on his face that Tara would dearly have loved to wipe off. She noticed a gold filling ludicrously occupying a gap between two heavily-discoloured teeth. She shuddered, but went forward when he said,

'Mr Leon says that I haf to show you the dining-saloon.'

She realised she was hungry, and realised too that she would gain nothing by staying that way—if she was allowed to.

The saloon was the last word in luxury, its walls of pine highly polished, and built-in furniture with, in one corner, a cocktail cabinet. The table was laid with gleaming silver and glass, and there was an appetising odour coming from the dishes standing on the side-board. Leon, looking even more distinguished than before in navy blue slacks and a white linen jacket, was standing by the cocktail cabinet, apparently absorbed in the perusal of a label on the bottle he held in his hand. He turned, flicking a hand in dismissal to his servant.

'Sit down,' he invited her. 'The meal's ready, but perhaps you would like a drink first?'

She shook her head.

'I don't want anything, thank you.'

'There's wine with the meal. You can have some of that.'

She opened her mouth to refuse, then closed it again as she saw his expression. His mouth was tight, his eyes faintly narrowed; she had seen that expression before.

He drew out a chair and she sat down, taking in the candles in their silver holders, the flowers expertly arranged.

'You had everything prepared,' she could not resist saying, acid in her tone.

'For a romantic dinner at sea?' His eyes held a vague hint of humour. 'Yes, I did have it all prepared. Elias—you've not met him yet, but you will in a moment—bought the flowers ready arranged, and the candles we already had——'

'In stock—for an occasion such as this. I suppose you've had dozens of loose women on board this boat.'

'I'd prefer you not to refer to them as loose,' he returned darkly. 'Yes, I have had intimate dinners aboard with my women friends.' He took possession of the chair opposite to her and stretched his long legs under the table. He clapped his hands and a man appeared instantly.

'We'll have the first course now, Elias. And tell Dimitri to pour the wine.'

'How many men are on board this boat?' enquired Tara, amazed that she was so calmly accepting the situation in which she found herself. She was hungry, and actually looking forward to eating a meal—though not in this man's hateful company, of course.

'Three. It's not the usual number for the crew of a vessel of this size, but I needed to limit the men to those I knew for sure I could trust implicitly. None of them will ever say a word of what has happened on this trip. Dimitri's the man who was driving the first taxi.'

'He is?' Her mouth tightened and a sparkle came to her eyes. 'If only we'd had some suspicion. . . .'

'How could you? You ordered cars for the wedding and they were provided. Why should you ever have suspected that one of them was driven by my servant?'

She made no answer, and in any case Dimitri was there, pouring the wine, while Elias served smoked salmon as the first course. Dimitri spoke to Leon in Greek; Tara's eyes glinted and she spoke on impulse.

'I suppose,' she said acidly, 'you're talking about the clever way you helped in my abduction!'

The man turned, his dark eyes sliding from her white face to that of his employer.

'I was merely carrying out the orders of my master,' he said quietly, in that same excellent English he had used when driving the taxi.

'It is all right, Dimitri——' Leon waved him away with a swift flick of his hand. The man went out, following in the wake of Elias whose brown face had all the while been creased in a smile of amusement. Hateful bunch of Greeks! Scoundrels, all of them!

'Don't they care about the law?' she flashed, glowering at the man opposite to her.

'They obey orders.' He spoke slowly, his black eyes never leaving her face. 'As you will obey me when I order you not to speak like that again to any of my servants. For one thing, it's undignified. I won't allow my wife to lose her dignity with anyone else but me. Understand?'

Fury burned colour into her cheeeks.

'You are the last person I'd lower my dignity for!' One hand was resting on the snow-white tablecloth

and before she could even guess at his intention he had
rapped her sharply over the knuckles with the blade of
his knife. It was no gentle tap and involuntarily she
cried out, tears springing to her eyes, as much from the
shock of the unexpected as from the pain inflicted.

'Take heed from that,' warned Leon darkly. 'Guard
your tongue if you want to avoid punishment.' He
looked at her plate, then his eyes came back to her face.
'Dry your eyes, and then eat your salmon,' he ordered
curtly.

She brought out a handkerchief—the dainty lacy
thing which Sue had slipped into the cuff of her wedding-dress. She stared at it, scarcely able to believe what
had happened to her since Sue had said, half in
humour, half in gravity,

'It's not unusual for a bride to be so affected by
emotion that a tear comes to her eye, so we shall take
the precaution of providing you with this.'

A terrible lump rose in Tara's throat as she put the
handkerchief to her eyes, but instead of using it she
wept uncontrollably into it.

An exclamation of asperity came from the other side
of the table.

'What in the name of Hades is wrong with you now?'
he wanted to know. 'Good God, girl, don't you ever
stop crying!'

'I h-have—plenty—to—to cry—about,' she sobbed,
aware that the handkerchief was useless. Her serviette
was on her knee and she took it up. But to her amazement Leon was there, at her side, and he pulled her
gently to her feet and in a moment her eyes had been
dried with his handkerchief. Absurdly she found herself saying,

'Th-thank y-you.'

He tilted her chin, bent his dark head, and kissed
her on the lips.

'Sit down and compose yourself,' he said gently.

'Elias will be back in a few minutes.'

Tara stared at him as he sat down, unable to determine whether his features really had lost most of their hardness or whether the mist in her eyes made it appear so. But certainly it had been a kindly intention that had prompted him to come over and dry her eyes. What a contradictory character he had! Never in a thousand years would she have expected the gentleness she had just received at his hands.

For a while she ate in silence, and then, looking up, she asked a trifle anxiously,

'Where is my wedding-dress?'

'Does it matter?' he queried in a casual tone of voice.

'I—I don't th-think it does. But I'd like to have kept it.'

'What for? You will not be wearing it when you marry me.' The inflexibility in his voice erased all the gentleness that had gone before. She wondered if it had been a momentary lapse because, looking at him now, with his features stern and forbidding, it seemed impossible that kindness could be one of his traits.

'I don't know what for,' she admitted, glad that the sobs in her throat were subsiding, and she could speak without stammering. 'I can't think properly. I would like to keep my wedding-dress, though.'

'A morbid sentimentality. It's down among the fishes,' he added heartlessly. 'A pretty thing in its way, but not you at all. What made you choose a style like that?'

'Because I happened to like it!' she shot at him, feeling that if she tried to suppress her rising anger she would burst into tears again, because of what he had done with her beautiful wedding-dress. 'A girl usually has the right to choose the style of her own wedding-dress!'

'You liked it?' He shook his head and frowned. 'You will have to be educated,' he told her decisively. 'Your taste is incredibly unimaginative. You could look like a queen, given the correct styles and colours. Your hair will have to be cut,' he decided as his eyes lit on it. 'I'm not partial to hair quite as long as that. Did your fiancé like to bury his face in it, or something? For myself, it's all right, but I'd much rather bury my face in a warmer, more seductive place.' His black eyes went to her breasts and a satirical light entered them as he saw the swift and painful rise of colour to her face.

'You're nothing but a beast——'

'Careful, Tara,' came the softly-spoken interruption. 'It was only your knuckles that were rapped just now, but it will be somewhere very different next time.'

Her colour deepened. If only she dared get up and leave the table! But caution kept her where she was.

She said after a long pause,

'The way you talk about clothes it would seem that you always dress your women to suit *your* tastes? Am I to be another puppet?'

The words appeared to amuse him and she was puzzled as to the reason.

'My taste is considered perfect,' he rejoined casually. 'As for my models being puppets—well, I suppose that in a way they are. It is I who pull the strings and they who dance for me.'

Tara could only stare at him for several seconds, staggered by the man's insufferable pomposity.

'You'll never get me to dance for you,' she retorted at last. 'I've no idea what sort of women you've had, but they certainly lacked spirit!' She was becoming more composed now, a circumstance for which she was glad, since at least she was not showing him a weak side of her character which was not true to form anyway. Her career as a nurse in a very large hospital had, if only to a small extent, given her a certain toughness she would never have come by otherwise.

'They did lack spirit,' Leon agreed, 'which you do

not, in spite of the copious tears you've been shedding.
I believe we shall get along most successfully once you
resign yourself to the fact that you've gained rather
than lost by my action in abducting you.' His hard
Greek eyes fixed hers as he held out a silver basket con-
taining crispy bread rolls. 'Freshly baked in the galley
by Carlos,' he told her. 'That man can turn his hand to
anything.'

'Including taking illegal part in his master's nefari-
ous schemes,' Tara just could not help retorting.

'You, my girl, will get another rap over the knuckles
if you don't guard that venomous tongue of yours. How
many more times do you need to be warned?' His knife
was in his hand, his eyes on *her* hand as it lay on the
cloth. Hastily she moved it, an automatic reaction,
and she gritted her teeth as she heard him laugh. She
picked up her glass and took a drink.

'How long does it take to get to this island you live
on?'

'Some fair time,' was his non-committal reply, and
then he paused in thought. 'I've a friend on the island
of Corfu who'll marry us—a priest of the Greek Ortho-
dox Church. I saved his life once and quite unneces-
sarily he lives in a state of perpetual gratitude. He has
often said that he feels obligated to me and that if ever
he can repay me he will go to any lengths to do so.'

'I can't believe his gratitude would go to the lengths
you speak of.'

'He'll marry us and ask no questions.'

'Another criminal, then?—living under the cloak of
the church.' With every moment that passed she was
gaining a little more composure. It was as if some in-
built power was functioning to help her through her
ordeal, guarding her against the total collapse which at
first she had believed was inevitable owing to the
ghastly upheaval in her life brought about by this
ruthless Greek pagan sitting opposite to her.

'He's a most devout Christian,' rejoined Leon in answer to her comment.

'But not troubled by the fate of his soul, apparently.'

Leon gave a gust of laughter.

'She has a sense of humour, too! Yes, my dear Tara, you and I will get along fine. You'll be more diverting than all the rest put together.' He was still amused; she had a strong suspicion that he was playing with her. She looked into his eyes, noticing that his thin cruel mouth was relaxed now into a sensual curve above a ruthless, out-thrust chin of great strength. There were hollows beneath his high cheekbones which added to the distinction of his features as a whole and it suddenly crossed her mind that Sue might have been right, after all, when she described him as handsome. Certainly he possessed the kind of face that would attract certain women ... those who craved to be mastered, thought Tara. For there was not one tiny sign of weakness to be found anywhere—even the deep lines across his dark forehead gave the impression of formidable invincibility.

She had compared him with David before and she found herself doing it again. There was such a vast difference in the two men and she did not know why she was comparing them. David was so kind and gentle and not particularly self-assertive; he almost always let her have her own way, which was very obliging of him and very comfortable for her. His kisses were gentle, respectful, his embrace tenderly relaxed, so that he should not hurt her at all. But this Greek—this heathen with the saturnine features and arrogant self-confidence of the god Zeus himself! This detestable creature did hurt her—he meant to hurt, purely to let her see who was master. His kisses were meant to be cruel, his hands ruthless, and even his voice was imperiously dictatorial, as if by it he would bend her to his iron-hard will.

'What are your thoughts at this moment, Tara?' His voice cut into her reverie and she looked at him. His glass was between his long lean fingers and he was regarding her with a faintly sardonic smile. 'I have an idea you were thinking about me.'

'How clever of you,' she returned with sarcasm. 'Yes, I was thinking how detestable you are!'

'And yet you promised to marry me,' was the suave reminder.

She went red to the roots of her hair.

'I never for one moment considered marrying you,' she denied.

'Liar. That night when you promised you were resigned to telling your fiancé, even at that late stage, that it was all a mistake and you could not marry him.'

'I was—was under the influence of—of——' She broke off painfully and, picking up her glass, she emptied it in one continuous swallow.

'Under the influence of love——'

'Rubbish!'

'I did not mean you to take the word quite literally. You were under the influence of desire, of my lovemaking. All you wanted at that moment was to get into bed with me.'

'Oh——! You're the most insufferable creature—and I hate you!'

'For voicing the truth?' He put the glass to his lips and took a small drink, then placed it on the coaster, his eyes never leaving her face. 'You're a coward, Tara, you're afraid to own that you can be as amorous, and as eager for the fulfilment of sex, as I can.'

'Shut up—be quiet——!' She put her hands to her ears, glowering at him. 'I don't want to listen—I won't listen!' And with that she flung herself off the chair and ran for the door. But he barred her way, seizing her round the waist and swinging her off her feet, then down and against the virile hardness of his body. 'Oh

... let me go——' His lips crushed with brutal dominance the rest of what she was going to say. His arms
brought her close, crushing her tender breasts against
the coiled-spring hardness of his chest. She gasped,
fighting for breath, gulping air when at last he drew his
sensuous, demanding mouth from hers. She felt her
ribs would collapse from the fiendish cruelty of his
hold. He was determined to prove his complete mastery
over her, to demonstrate the superiority of his strength.
His hands spanned her waist as eventually he held her
at arms' length, his eyes burning, a betrayal of the
smouldering desire within him. He wanted her—desperately! Fear rose in great waves of mental agony as
she lived in imagination what must surely come to her.
She closed her eyes, willing herself not to cry out for
mercy, not to plead and whimper, revealing her weakness while her strength lay dormant, reduced to inert-
ness by this man's powerful, magnetic personality.

'Admit it!' he commanded, his voice vibrant with
passion. 'Admit that you did want to marry me—that
you would have done so if we could have gone off at
that time! I ought to have taken you—brought you to
surrender so that you'd have had proof of your own
desires.' His hands slid down to her thighs, infusing life
into her body, stimulating her emotions in a deliberate
attempt to bring her to submission. 'Admit that you
wanted me—that you want me at this moment!' So
arrogant, so dictatorial his voice. She tried to twist
away, but he held her easily as he slid his hands to her
waist again. The next moment she was locked to him,
melded to his body, her quivering lips were parted in
obedience to the sensuous demands of his, and quivers
of sheer ecstasy rippled along her spine. She was
ordered to put her arms around his neck and as before
she obeyed. From the deep mist of her drugged mind
she was recalling the night he had mentioned, and soon
she was re-living it, thrilling to the hardness of his body

in its erotic unrest, to the contact of his warm fingers caressing her breast, to the temptation of his other hand as it slid lower and lower down her back.

'Admit it,' he ordered again hoarsely, and she had no resistance to defy him ... she had no desire to defy him. She was ready to surrender in any way he should command and he knew it; she was ready to become his wife and he heard her say it.

'We shall pull in at Corfu,' he said a moment later when, hearing Dimitri and Elias talking outside the door, he released her and told her to sit down. 'We'll be married very soon, Tara, and all your desires will be fulfilled.'

# CHAPTER FIVE

HE came to her cabin, as she expected he would. But the intervening time since the moment when she had said she wanted to marry him, and the end of the meal, had brought Tara well and truly to her senses. She admitted that the Greek with his vast experience of women and the finesse which, apparently had always proved successful, could ignite within her a flame of desire which could rise to a conflagration that would destroy her altogether. Sanity came swiftly, with its cold logic, and by the time the coffee and cognac were served to them in the main saloon—which was the sitting-room—she was ready to do battle with him again. Her composure was restored, and her dignity. She accepted the fact of her own weakness where his persuasions were concerned but resolved firmly never to be caught off balance again. She would fight him all the way, would control her impulses somehow.

She was pale but totally composed when, hearing the door handle turn, she swung around to see Leon in the doorway, a tall impressive figure with teak-brown skin, black piercing eyes and a smile on his thin lips that was a mixture of triumph and amusement.

'Not ready for me?' he observed with a lift of his straight black brows. 'Shall I be lady's maid for you, my dear ... ?' He was closing the door behind him as he spoke, and in spite of her resolve Tara was already affected by his magnetic presence. What had he done to her? How could any man have this kind of power? Did every woman he met fall beneath it?

'I—I've changed my mind about marrying you,' she managed to say, amazed that her voice was steady. 'I don't know why you've come, but——'

'Tara,' he chided in a very soft tone, 'cut out the infantile innocence. You must admit it's more than a little ridiculous after all that happened in there, an hour or so ago. If I'd carried you to bed then you'd be my possession by now.'

'Possession! Greek women are their husbands' possessions, aren't they?'

'Married women are,' he answered mildly. 'It's as it should be, surely?'

'Who's pretending now?' demanded Tara. 'You've enough knowledge of the West to know that it is *not* as it should be!'

'You expect equality?' He shook his head. 'Not for you, Tara. I'm the master in my home—and everyone, including my wife—would forget it at their peril.' So unemotional the tone, but the dictatorial undercurrent could not possibly be missed.

'Please go,' said Tara wearily. 'I want to go to bed.'

'You're tired?' Something was obviously amusing him, but his face was an impenetrable mask, fixed, unreadable.

'Yes, I'm tired.'

'You wouldn't have been, though, if you were on your honeymoon?'

She gave a start. Was it only hours since this fiend had snatched her away from her waiting bridegroom? Tears started to her eyes. This night would have been. . . .

'Go away!' she cried. 'I hate your presence, your face, your rotten Greek arrogance. Go away, I said!'

Instead, he moved towards her and she retreated until the backs of her legs touched the bed.

'You're frustrated? Is that it? But there's no need——'

'Frustrated?' she broke in, puzzled.

'Feeling deprived—of the bedmate you've been looking forward for weeks to lying with. I've been through the experience myself once or twice. It's a bit of a let-down when you've banked on a passionate interlude that doesn't materialise.' Another step brought him closer, but then he stopped.

'*You* seem to know,' she flashed, playing for time.

'Of course I know. Women are so unpredictable; they often think they will and then decide they won't. Of course, any man worth his salt will accept the refusal as a challenge, but sometimes it's not worth the trouble.'

She looked at him; the suspicion crossed her mind that he was playing with her and she flushed, maintaining a silence she had no intention of breaking.

Leon broke it by saying,

'As I remarked, you have no need to be frustrated. I'm very sure I shall make a most excellent substitute for your bridegroom. In fact,' he added, slowly coming towards her, 'in your secret heart you prefer me to him.'

'You pompous, conceited—heathen!'

He was close enough for her to catch the odour of after-shave—a clean, healthy smell that reminded her of pine trees after rain. His hand was lifted and she flinched, expecting him to slap her cheek for what she had said, but instead he took her chin in a hard grip, bent his head and kissed her tightly-closed lips.

'When you're angry you are very appealing; I want to prolong your anger and yet, oddly enough, I want to bring you to heel. You're exciting, Tara, as I knew you would be on the very first occasion I set eyes on you.' Releasing her, he moved away; she missed the contact of his hand on her chin, of his nearness, of the touch of his lips. . . .

She said after a moment,

'Will you please go?'

'You have just promised to marry me,' he reminded her. 'I don't think it's necessary to wait, do you? We can begin our honeymoon now——'

'It was two hours ago that I said I'd marry you,' she broke in, fear widening her eyes because of his glance, which swept its amorous way from her face to her neck and then to the firm contours of her breasts. 'I've changed my mind. I shall never marry you, never!'

The black eyes kindled and the thin nostrils quivered. He reminded her of an untamed jungle beast ready to pounce on its terror-stricken prey. Oh, God, how had she got herself into a position like this! Such things only happened to other people. You read about them in the newspapers, felt sorry for the victim, then tossed the paper aside. You weren't affected; you never even dreamed of being the victim yourself.

And now, in England, people would be reading about *her*—the bride who had been kidnapped on her way to her wedding. What a dramatic headline it would make for the morning papers—an interesting story to be read at the breakfast table. And poor David frantic. For the first time in her life Tara was glad that she had no parents.

'You will marry me—and enjoy being my wife.' The low, alien voice drifted into her thoughts; she could have wept to hear the throaty bass note which he made no attempt to hide. 'Come on,' he coaxed, 'relax and take what's offered. I can promise you'll enjoy this night far more than if you were with that fellow you were going to marry.'

'Go away! I can't think properly! Can't you see my heart is breaking?'

An exasperated little intake of his breath, an impatient flash of his eyes and then,

'Hearts never break! For heaven's sake try to get rid of this dogged determination to suffer! It's an attitude of mind,' he added derisively, 'nothing more!'

'You have no heart,' she quavered, 'that's why you can't understand.'

'I understand how I can make you forget——' And
with a swift movement he drew her shrinking body to
him, his arms pinning it against him as he sought her
lips, forcing their tightness apart. Tara writhed and
twisted, fighting with everything in her, pitifully en-
gaging herself in a losing battle. She could feel the wild
throbbing of her heart and it frightened her; she knew
the exquisite pain of a cruel, possessive embrace, the
pleasure-pain of a breast being ruthlessly fondled.
Leon's passion rose to unbridled heights and his kisses
were fire on her lips. She knew she must surrender even
before his strength had taken all the physical fight out
of her.

'Passive at last,' he murmured, his mouth warm and
soft against her breast. 'What strength you have, child
—but it makes the victory all the more satisfying.' He
lifted his head to stare with amused triumph into eyes
dark and cloudy with desire. 'You said you'd changed
your mind about marrying me, but you haven't, have
you?' While he spoke his hand was bringing down the
zip fastener of her dress and she quivered ecstatically
at the contact of his fingers with her back. She was
totally trapped in a net of sensual yearning, unable to
think of anything save the glorious temptation of the
moment. Never in her life had she been affected with
emotions of such violent intensity. Her forehead was
damp, with tendrils of hair clinging to it. Excitement
throbbed in every vein ... and David was a million
light years away.... 'Have you ... my little tiger cat?'
repeated Leon, and she lifted her lovely face and said
in a voice that held not a trace of uncertainty,

'No, Leon, I haven't changed my mind about marrying you.'

'You want to marry me—say it.'

'I want to marry you.'

The dress left her body and she stood before his gaze,
colour filtering into her cheeks.

'How beautiful you are.' Leon traced the pattern of her mouth and chin, his touch feather-soft as it reached her breast. One strap of her bra was slipped down and he looked his fill—and suddenly his gaze seemed lecherous. She found a tangle of thoughts and ideas spiralling in her mind, pictures of scenes such as this, but with other women involved. Sickeningly she was thinking: how many women's breasts has he looked upon as he's looking upon mine now? She saw these women as she was, totally under the domination of this man, their will-power sapped beneath the lustful, animal strength of his. And, lastly, she saw David, and an hotel bedroom where she was running willingly into his gentle, loving arms.

A terrible shuddering seized her near naked body and a flood of tears, which must surely have been gathered in a cloud behind her eyes all the time, was released, blinding her vision.

'What the hell's wrong now!' The fury in his voice came over to her, but that in his black eyes had to be imagined. She was sobbing hysterically and in his anger he did no more than grip her by the shoulders and shake her. 'Pull yourself together!' he thundered. 'So much can be endured, but this is beyond everything! A moment ago you were happy, and now this absurd weeping. Pull yourself together, I say!'

She rubbed at her eyes and could see him as if through a mist. At least, she thought with a vague sense of wonder, his ardour seemed to have cooled. When she spoke it was in the soft, sweetly-modulated voice which David had so loved. And she said what was in her heart at this particular moment.

'Can't you see, Leon, how it is with me? This was to have been my honeymoon night, the night that David and I would remember all our lives, no matter what pleasures were to come later.' Her beautiful eyes, bright with tears, looked appealingly into his. 'But instead of what I'd so eagerly looked forward to, I'm here, in the power of another man, a man who doesn't love me, who has made my wedding day one of blackness and despair, who's even thrown away my lovely dress— wh-which a w-woman saves and treasures, Leon, although you would not understand——' She broke off as a great sob shook her body from head to foot. 'It would be dishonest if I were to deny that you can tempt me, can force me to say things I don't mean—like—like wanting to marry you.' Again she looked appealingly up into his face, noticing this time that although it was taut and forbidding it was by no means harsh. And at a little point in his throat a pulse seemed to be throbbing, as if it were an outlet for some kind of emotion. 'Is it likely that I would mean it when I say I'll marry you? I'm in love with someone else—Oh, don't be angry!' she cried, seeing his expression change. 'I beg of you not to get—get into a temper with me again. I can't stand much more—surely even you can see that?'

To her relief the fury that had darkened his face was only fleeting. He was listening again, intently, to what she was saying. 'My heart is breaking, no matter what you believe. Here! It—it hurts, Leon....' She put a hand to her breast, feeling the wild throbbing of her heart. Leon seemed spellbound, his dark eyes fixed, staring at the trembling hand that lay against her heaving breast. 'Don't hurt me any more,' she pleaded. 'Go away and leave me—if you have any sensibility at all you'll do as I ask.'

He moved, to pick up the négligé he had bought her and which lay across the bottom of the bed. To her surprise he held it open and automatically she slipped into it. He turned her round, his long brown fingers gentle on her arms, arms he had bruised only moments ago when he had shaken her. She looked up, her eyes still moist with tears. He was fastening the neck of the négligé with the ribbons attached to it, then a couple of buttons. His eyes were dark, unfathomable. Everything about him was strange. It was a tense and oddly intimate moment that held them both before he said, flicking away a tear that was falling,

'Rest well—if you can, Tara. I hope you will feel better tomorrow.' He went to the door and opened it. 'Good night, child,' he said gruffly. 'Try not to cry any more.'

And with those words he was gone, leaving her drained, exhausted, and in that mental state whereby she would have welcomed death and the blessed oblivion that it would give to her.

As was to be expected, sleep eluded her, but in spite of her deep misery and anguish of heart, there had come to her the realisation that her plight could have been a great deal worse. Leon, though he was a callous brute in her eyes—and always would be—had not turned out to be the fearful rapist that he might have been. During the long dark hours of the night when the only sound was the throbbing of the boat's engine, she had lain there thinking, her mind a turmoil of thoughts that flitted about, sometimes starkly isolated from one another, and at other times mingling into a tangled network which she could not hope to unravel. Leon's behaviour was the most isolated thought, and the most baffling. That he could have worked himself up into that state of passionate desire and then held back was well nigh a miracle to Tara. His control must be incredible, for there was nothing to prevent his taking her. Moreover, he was well aware that, when her paroxysm of distress was at an end, he could be almost sure she would have come to him willingly, so great was his power over her, his ability to awaken in her a hunger that would have to be appeased.

Her thoughts had switched quite naturally to what might have been—the wedding in the church, and bells pealing out, bringing women and children running from the nearby houses to see the glowing bride come from the church on the arm of her groom. She had known she would be conscious of this activity, and would revel in the fact that it was her those people had come to see, because it was *her* lovely day, the one day in her life that would be re-lived more than any other. There was the buffet at the best hotel in town, with the photographer there to make sure the cutting of the cake was recorded for the 'Wedding Book'. And the toasts, the sincere wishes for their happiness. After that she would change, helped by Sue, and the car would take them to the airport from where they would fly to Scotland ... for their honeymoon.... What were David's emotions? she had wondered. He too would be lying awake, dwelling on what might have been. Tara had cried out to him in the darkness of the cabin which was her prison, willing the message to reach him, telling him she still loved him and that, one day, she would fight her way back to him.

Yes, escape was the next isolated thought that occupied her mind. She could not believe that her captor could keep her prisoner for very long. That he would make her marry him she was beginning to accept, and she knew too that, given the choice of being his wife or his pillow-friend, she would be bound to choose the former. And so it did seem that marriage to him was to be her fate—but she would escape eventually, and she prayed that the opportunity would come soon. Of course, she naturally cherished the hope that escape would come before she was forced into marriage, but the recollection of his methods up till now tended to dash this hope and send her into the depths of hopelessness and resignation. For he had been successful beyond belief in every move he had made.

The following morning she was up and dressed when he came to the cabin. He looked her over with a frown.

'You've not slept,' he observed. He was in white slacks and a navy blue blazer with an anchor badge on the breast pocket. She looked at him and it seemed impossible to reconcile this tall, refined and cool-voiced man with the bestial qualities which at times he could reveal.

'No,' she replied unsteadily, 'but it was not to be expected that I would.' She did not know of the wistful expression in her eyes, or that there was a sort of haunting beauty and charm in the sadness of her face. She did see the pulsation of a nerve in Leon's bronzed throat but never questioned the reason for it.

'In Greece,' said Leon, reaching out to take hold of her hand, 'we have a rather pleasing little saying—the Greeks were famous for their eloquence at one time, as you probably know.'

She continued to stare at him, confused by his manner, wondering where the arrogance was, the taunting expression of amusement to which she was so often subjected.

'What is this saying?' she asked when he did not speak.

'We quarrel sometimes and then we "make harmony". Let you and me make harmony, Tara. It will be more comfortable for both of us.'

Her mouth trembled, because she was affected by the change in him, the kind expression in his eyes, the request that they make harmony. The misery that had grown and flourished since the moment of her abduction seemed in some small way to be lessened by his change of manner towards her.

'I—well, if you want us to,' she began, looking down with shadowed eyes to the hand that held hers.

'I do want us to,' he assured her, an odd inflection in his voice. 'Shall we seal it with a kiss?' She was shaking her head as he bent his. She felt his kiss, gentle ... almost tender.

Something hurt in the region of her heart and she could not account for it. She felt she could actually have come to like him had they met in circumstances other than those which had resulted in her present plight.

'I don't understand you,' she faltered. 'You're—so different this morning.'

The black eyes seemed one second to brood and the next to frown. That his emotions were mixed was evident, and his next words strengthened the idea.

'For the first time in my life, Tara, I don't understand myself!' And he appeared to be rather angry about it, as if to be baffled by his own behaviour was a circumstance exceedingly irritating to him. 'If you are ready we'll have breakfast—and don't say you're not hungry,' he warned sternly but not unkindly, 'because I shall make you eat something whether you like it or not.'

She went meekly with him, overcome with relief at the change in his attitude towards her which made her feel some element of safety for the first time since he had snatched her from under the nose of her escort.

And the change continued, with Leon obviously intending to honour their pact to 'make harmony'. He said goodnight each evening and let her go to bed unmolested; he seemed at times to look at her critically, as if wanting to see a disappearance of the sad and strained expression which she wore all the time. On one occasion he had seemed to become impatient—as if he just could not help it—and had ordered her to smile, which she did, reluctantly, then asked what difference a smile could make either to her feelings or her situation.

'You're stubborn, Tara. No matter what you think, I did save you from a disastrous marriage.'

She shrugged impatiently.

'How can you know how David and I felt about one another?'

'I happen to know the kind of man who will satisfy you.'

'That man could never be you,' she told him firmly.

'We shall see. Once we are married you'll taste the real fruits of physical pleasure.'

'So—so you haven't changed your mind?' she said bleakly.

'About what?' They were on deck, he in shorts and sandals and Tara in a bikini he had told her to wear.

'I thought that perhaps you might be considering taking me back.'

'Not a chance, my child. I want you and have gone to a great deal of trouble to get you. Your destiny is to be my wife, the mother of my sons——'

'No! I don't want your children!'

The dark eyes bored into her, so that she was compelled to lower hers, and absently she began to trace a pattern on the boarded deck.

'Nevertheless, you *will* have my children,' he said implacably, 'because it is my intention that you shall. Marriage without children lacks something vitally important.'

'Important to what?' She glanced sharply at him, puzzled by the inflection in his voice, for although it was stern and dictatorial there was an underlying element which, she felt, would be important if only she could understand it.

'To the success of the marriage,' he answered after a pause which made her suspect that the words he had uttered were different from those that had previously lingered on his tongue. Had he been going to say important to 'happiness'? she wondered, and as a result of this idea she said,

'Don't you consider happiness important in marriage?'

There was a strange silence after that which lasted for perhaps half a minute. What was he thinking about? Tara felt tensed, expectant, as if she were about to make a discovery. But it was a fleeting sensation which passed, and was to be forgotten for ever.

'We shall be calling at Corfu tomorrow,' he told her, deliberately changing the subject. 'I shall go ashore and seek out my friend, the priest, who will come aboard to marry us.'

Her heart sank to the depths, and every inch of her body went cold.

'You didn't tell me we were so close to Corfu,' she faltered, white to the lips.

'You had no need to know,' he returned casually. 'I'm fully aware that at each place where we've stopped for fuel you have cherished the hope of escape, but by now you will, I think, have accepted that I am thorough, and that my crew are very careful to carry out my orders, which are that you are to be watched all the time that we are in any port. At Corfu you'll be locked in your cabin, as is usual when we're in port.'

She twisted her hands distractedly.

'I don't want to marry you,' she whispered, swallowing hard because of the dryness that had settled in her throat, 'For God's sake, let me go! I've promised I will keep silent——'

'How would you explain your absence?' he broke in, his eyes flickering with interest.

'I'd think of something!' she returned wildly. 'I lost my memory—people often do!'

'Don't be silly,' he chided as if talking to someone little more than a baby. 'You were abducted, remember?'

'I'm not likely to forget—not ever as long as I live!'

'Perhaps one day you will regard it as a very fortunate occurrence in your life.' He spoke casually, lifting an indolent hand to smother a yawn. 'You will wear the dress I bought in Lisbon. The colour's delightful for you, and so is the style. You like it?' he added as if the thought had just occurred to him.

She shook her head dumbly, thinking of her beautiful bridal gown, perfected after several fittings and now lying at the bottom of the sea. The dress Leon had bought—among many others collected at the ports where they had stopped to refuel—was coral-gold with a tight-fitting bodice and finely-pleated skirt. The sleeves were long and full, gathered into a narrow cuff. It was a model of perfection which she felt she hated, now that her captor had decided it was to be her wedding dress.

'It's all right,' she mumbled, realising he was waiting for an answer. 'Is there no way I can persuade you to let me go?' He shook his head, frowning, and before he had time to speak she was saying in a loud and vibrant voice,

'This man shall not marry us! I'll threaten him—and although you can keep me prisoner you can't imprison my tongue! I shall put so much fear into him that he'll refuse to marry us, no matter what his obligation is to you!'

He looked at her imperturbably.

'If you do protest,' he said quietly, 'then I shall send him away.'

'Yes?'

'And you will from that night on become my mistress.' She said nothing, because she had known of the choice she would have to make, had been fully aware that all these protestations and threats were worthless against the whip-hand held by this heartless and determined foreigner.

'He's coming aboard, you say?'

'Of course. Is it likely that I would risk taking you ashore?'

'I've no choice then, but to—to marry you?' It seemed impossible that anyone could force another person into marriage, and yet it was the case. Marriage or ... the other. Well, marriage it would have to be, but she would think of nothing but escape until that escape was effected.

# CHAPTER SIX

TARA first saw the island of Hyra in the sunset glow of early evening. One of the 'Siren Isles' of the Saronic Gulf, it appeared from out of the sea like a mermaid floating on the calm waves, and despite her situation she found herself showing interest in the place where she was to live. Leon had told her a little of the island's history, so she knew it had once been the haunt of brave buccaneering men but that in recent years many writers, artists and ship-owners had been attracted to its shores. The big houses on the hillsides were owned by the wealthy, and had been for many years. Leon's home was one of these. She had learned that he was a ship-owner but that he had interests elsewhere, and one of these interests was fashion. The House of Hera, famous for feminine clothes of distinction, belonged to him. This information, given to her casually, explained his previous use of the word 'models', and of the assertion that his taste was considered perfect. He himself designed many of the exclusive gowns for which the House of Hera had become world-famed. This knowledge of his possessing artistic qualities had had an unexpected effect on Tara, since from then on she had re-regarded him less of a monster than before. All the same, her one all-absorbing idea was that of escape, and this, she felt, might be possible on landing on the island.

She was standing by the rail when Leon came up to her.

'When we get a little closer I'll point out our house to you.'

She stiffened. *Our* house.... A fluttering sensation

affected her stomach, for somehow his words had the sort
of finality about them which seemed to mean that her
whole future was mapped out and there was nothing
in the world that could alter it. She was her husband's
possession; that was *their* house; she would be installed
in it and from then on she would be nothing more than
a slave, a chattel, like most women of the East. There
was desperation in her voice as, turning to him and unconsciously brushing his face with her hair, she retorted,

'*Your* house, you mean! It can never be our house!'

He frowned down at her, his mouth going tight.

'What is this?' he demanded sharply. 'Are you still
thinking that you will run from me?'

'I'd be a poor specimen of womanhood if I were to
accept this bondage you're holding me in. Of course I
shall try to escape!'

For a moment it seemed that he would lose his temper, but to her surprise the tightness went from his
mouth and the glint from his eyes.

'I've already assured you that you will thank me one
day,' he said. 'We shall probably have a child before
very long—there might even be one on the way now—
and then perhaps you will become resigned to your
lot.'

Tara's teeth came together. A child on the way!
Strange that through several nights of passion the idea
had not once come to her. Oh, God, please don't let
that happen to me! she thought. Could she ever hope
to escape if that did happen? Leon would never allow
her to take his child from him, and she felt sure she
could never leave it.

'I only pray I shall be spared that,' she told him
quiveringly. 'You seem to have forgotten that I love
another man! You've made me your wife, but you'll
regret it! I swear to you you'll regret it!'

'So, if you did escape you'd go to the police? Is that

what you are telling me?' Ice edged his voice and his eyes took on a matching glacier hardness.

'I would,' she stated firmly, undaunted by the severity of his face. 'I wouldn't have done if you'd let me go when I first begged you to, but now I shall! And that criminal of a priest will go to jail along with you!'

'What did he do? You never even made a murmur when he was marrying us.'

'Because of what you threatened me with,' she returned chokingly. 'But he must have known there was something phoney about the marriage – he possesses average intelligence, surely?'

'He did nothing illegal,' persisted Leon. 'You'll leave his name out of it ... if ever you do manage to escape.'

'So you don't regard escape as an impossibility? That's encouraging. Thank you very much for giving me hope!'

He looked out to the island and was silent for a moment before turning back to her and saying,

'If *my* hopes materialise you will have a child before very long, and then I can be sure you won't leave me.'

She turned away, tears starting to her eyes. Up till now all his plans had come to fruition, so why should she be optimistic enough to hope that this one would go away?

'As I said,' she quivered at last, 'I pray I shall never have a child of yours.'

'There is nothing wrong with either of us,' was his quiet rejoinder, 'so it's reasonable to assume that you will have my child within the year.' She said nothing and he turned her face to him, his cruel fingers gripping her chin so hard that she knew there would be bruises within a minute or two. 'I shall make you have my child, Tara. Do you understand? I'm your master; from now on I control your life. You will have as many children as I decide you shall have.'

'I'm to be your chattel, then!' she flashed, a conflagration of fury stemming from the humiliation of having to listen to his arrogant assertion. 'A slave! Oh, but I shall get away one day! You're a fool if you think you can keep me a prisoner for ever!'

He turned away from her and she put a trembling hand to her chin. Tears sparkled on her lashes, tears of misery and despair. For he knew his strength, and her weakness, was confident that if she did have a child she could never leave him.

She saw him walking away, arrogance even in the strides he took and the way his head was held. Proud aristocrat that he was, he could not change the vile traits he had inherited along with that pride! For a moment she found herself dwelling on that temporary change that had come over him on the first night aboard the boat. That he had intended taking her seemed at one time a certainty, but for some reason her tears and pleading had softened him and he had amazed her by leaving the cabin. His voice and manner had been gentle, and it did seem that he was concerned about her. During the days that followed he had kept to his intention of living in harmony with her, but the rift had been opened again when he said they were nearing Corfu and that the priest would marry him. The finality of his words had wrenched every vestige of hope from her heart, she recalled. The rift had widened still more on their wedding night, simply because she had fought him with every ounce of her strength. He had completely mastered her, brought her to heel, as he termed it, and although she never after that showed any physical aversion, he had sensed with that over-perceptive mind of his that she was fighting mentally, standing out against total surrender to his will.

He had taunted her with assertions that her resistance was nil against his technique, that she craved his lovemaking, enjoying the fulfilment just as much as he. She squirmed under the knowledge that it was

true, every word he said. And even when he arrogantly
stated that David could never have taken her to the
heights to which he was transporting her, she again
had to admit that he spoke the truth. David with
his gentle, restrained approach would not even know
how to begin the kind of lovemaking at which Leon
was so practised.

The island was coming closer as the crew brought
the *Catana* towards the harbour. Tara, determinedly
transferring her attention to the sights that met her
eyes, noticed the brightly-coloured caiques and white-
sailed yachts, swaying gently against the breeze. High
above the harbour rose the impressive mass of Mount
Prophet Elias, rocky and barren against the pearl-
mauve glow of the darkening sky. In spite of her
misery Tara could not help appreciating the beauty
that was spread out before her eyes. The mansions rose
one above another on the tree-clad plateau in the cliffs,
while the humbler blue and white cubic houses nestled
on the lower slopes or were strung out along the waterfront, a tall white campanile telling of the presence of
the church. There were no roads on the island which
could take traffic—just tracks up the mountainside
trodden by donkeys, and steps used by the occupiers
of the houses. Tara had supposed this to be unique, but
Leon had told her that there were a number of Greek
islands which were so mountainous that it was impossible to have traffic on them.

'Our house is there.' He had come to stand beside her
again, with that cat-like stealth which had earlier
caused her to compare him with a jungle beast. He was
pointing to a magnificent mansion standing on a large
plateau facing the harbour and the blue sea of the
Saronic Gulf beyond.

'It must have a wonderful view,' was all she said, and
thought that if she were coming to a place like this with
the man she loved she would have felt herself to be the

most fortunate woman in the world.

'I hope you will find it all to your liking, Tara. It's to be your permanent home from now on, so it will be better if you try to adapt yourself to the life you will be living.'

'I'm to be kept a prisoner, of course. It's puzzled me how you'll manage that, but I expect you have a plan, and that your plan will work—just as your others have.' she ended bitterly.

'My servants will be told that you suffer from a nervous disorder which has the effect of making you want to wander off all by yourself. I am naturally most perturbed, and anxious that you shall come to no harm, so I expect them to keep an eye on you all the time. I have two gardeners who will watch you when you're outside, and Pelayia, who will be your personal maid as well as having other tasks to do, will keep an eye on you when you are in the house—watching that you don't go any further than the grounds.'

Tara stared at him, anger bringing colour to her face. And yet, conversely, she was compelled to extend him a certain degree of admiration.

'How very clever of you! And what if I tell them it's all a pack of lies?'

A sardonic expression entered his eyes.

'Do you suppose they'll take your word before that of the man they have known for years? Do you imagine that any one of them is going to risk his or her job by allowing you to stray away?'

She looked at him through narrowed eyes.

'Do they really take your word?' she queried with intent interest in his expression. 'What you're really saying is that when you give them an order they obey it, blindly—not bothering to ask themselves what's at the root of the order?'

He inclined his head in a gesture of assent.

'They are paid by me. Work on this island is not

easy to come by, which tends to make people hold on tenaciously to the jobs they have. I am confident, Tara, that you will be well cared for. No one is going to let you stray away.'

She drew a deep breath.

'You believe you can have a watch kept upon me for twenty-four hours of every day?'

The corners of his mouth lifted in a smile of amusement.

'I myself shall be keeping a watch on you for a good portion of that time,' he drawled. 'From dinner time every day till after breakfast the next morning you will be my companion.'

She shot him a venomous glance as embarrassed colour mounted her cheeks.

'My chief jailer, eh!'

'Be careful,' he advised in a very soft voice. 'Don't go too far. Your husband is not a patient man.' Without giving her an opportunity of saying anything to that he walked away again. She turned her attention once more to the harbour and the boats lying in its shelter. But soon her erratic thoughts were wandering and she was wondering what David was doing at this moment. Was his agonised imagination creating pictures of what might have happened to her—rape, torture, and even death? Was he waiting in unbearable torment for news that her body had been found in a field or ditch? He would naturally fear the worst, losing hope with each day that passed. And over a fortnight had gone by since that fateful day....

Would David ever find out that she was married? If she escaped, yes, and the marriage would be annulled, while Leon served his prison sentence. It was a pity that the days of hard labour had gone, she thought spitefully. And it would do him the world of good to be fed on bread and water! She saw him returning and could willingly have done him a physical injury. She visualised pushing him overboard, and watching him drown.

Coming up to her again he said casually,

'You're very thoughtful, Tara.'

She nodded and said in response,

'Yes, I was thinking that I'd enjoy seeing you down there in the water, being attacked by a shark.'

'I don't believe you're as bloodthirsty as that,' he returned with a laugh, then added that there were no sharks in these waters.

'My day will come,' Tara warned him darkly.

'We shall see, my child. I'd take bets that within a month you'll have become so attached to me that you will take back those words.'

Pompous, self-opinionated creature! She turned her back on him, hoping the action would rid her of his presence. But she was gripped by the shoulders and jerked round to face him. His features were harsh, ruthless in their twisted, pagan expression; she saw the quiver of a thin nostril, the compression of his mouth and the unmistakable threat in those fierce black eyes. It seemed that a violent shudder passed through every part of her body, affecting every nerve. Shades of fear and distress darkened her eyes and her mouth twisted convulsively.

'Don't you ever turn your back on me again!' he snarled, shaking her mercilessly. 'You'll learn respect, my girl—or else!'

Tara swallowed over and over again, attempting to rid herself of this fearsome sensation of being in the power of Satan himself. Her mind was so numbed by fear that it was losing its hold on clear thought.

'Let me go,' she begged. 'You're hurting my shoulders!'

'There'll be more than your shoulders hurt if you treat me like that again!'

Tears glistened on her lashes as she looked at him; he released her, but his glowering expression remained.

She thought he would make her apologise and knew she would have to obey him if he made the order. But to her intense relief he remained silent, staring out towards the island, where lights were gaining strength as the sun sank lower, leaving its pale gold glow behind it, a glow that illuminated the drifting curls of gossamer cloud that fluttered across the sky. Darkness fell swiftly in this part of the world, her husband had told her, as there was no long-drawn-out period between the end of a full daylight and the onset of night. Already stars could be seen, and the suggestion of a crescent moon in the gathering mauve-pearl shades of dusk.

The boat was drawing close to the old-world harbour, and Tara could see the mansions more clearly—one-time homes of pirate traders who had acquired great wealth and entertained lavishly on the strength of it. In contrast to these patrician-like houses the small cubic villas with their white walls and bright blue shutters looked almost humble, yet even the humblest of them boasted hibiscus hedges, and beds of crotons and poinsettias. Tumbling over walls and trellises were masses of mauve and magenta bougainvillaeas, and in every garden there seemed to be citrus fruit trees.

When the boat docked darkness had fallen; there was no one about at all, and any hopes that Tara had retained were crushed as her husband, having taken her arm in a tight grip, told her that if she so much as made a sound he would take her back on the boat, lock her in her cabin and leave her there until the early hours of the morning when everyone would be in bed and asleep. It was no idle threat, and added to that there was the presence of three strong men besides the one who held her. She was led from the waterfront up a narrow rocky path, dark and steep. There was no chance of making a dash for it, she thought—and just as if he guessed what had crossed her mind Leon said unpleasantly,

'Try anything on, Tara, and I'll make sure you smart for a week or more.'

'I hate you!' she seethed, glancing back to see if his men were following. They were still on the boat; she could dimly discern their shadowy figures moving about. 'They're bringing the luggage,' said Leon. 'I collected you quite a wardrobe at the various ports we called at. However, you'll need a lot more. I'm anxious for you to wear some of our models.' By that he meant models created by the House of Hera, and it dawned on Tara that he was thinking of making her an advertisement for his clothes.

Eventually they reached the house, and the door was opened by a manservant who was obviously ready to welcome his master with a smile. But the smile faded as his dark Greek eyes lit on Tara.

'Meet my wife, Kleanthes. Tara, one of my servants.'

The man gaped, and said impulsively,

'Your wife, Kirie Leon! But what about Miss——' And then he managed to stop, a sort of horror on his face as he realised what he had said. Tara, slanting her husband a glance, saw his mouth compress, his eyes glimmer with anger. 'Welcome—Kiria Leon—Mrs Leon,' stammered Kleanthes, looking fearfully at his employer. He'd be in trouble over that slip, concluded Tara, wondering who this woman was, and if she would be cast off now that Leon had a wife. Perhaps he was not averse to having more than one woman at a time. She would not put it past the hateful beast! Kleanthes was speaking again as he stood aside for them to enter the high wide hall with its flowers and tapestry, its lovely antique furniture and Persian rugs scattered about the mosaic floor. 'Everyone will be very happy that Kirios Leon is having a wife at last! There will be plenty many sons—*ochi*!'

'Go to the devil!' returned Tara with an onrush of anger.

'To the devil——?' The man threw out his hands, looking to Leon for explanation. 'What is this—this go to the devil?'

'Mrs Leon is tired. Fetch Pelayia; she will show her to the bedroom.'

'Very good, Mr Leon! I go this minute!'

Turning, he almost ran—going to the kitchen, thought Tara, to relate the astounding news that Leon had brought home a wife.

'You had better learn to hold your tongue,' snapped Leon when the man was out of earshot. 'I've warned you about that before!'

'I'm not having a servant talking to me about sons!' she flared. 'Do you suppose I've no pride?'

'It's natural in my country to connect marriage with the coming of sons. You'll get used to the outspokenness of the Greeks.'

'The men?' with a glint in her eye. 'The women, I expect are dumb—kept under by their dictatorial husbands.'

'By God, you ask for it!' he gritted. 'I'd box your ears this very minute if I'd not sent for Pelayia!'

Tara sighed, making no comment as she looked around, deliberately attempting to calm her ruffled nerves by concentrating on something else. She noticed the old paintings on the walls, and the ikons, but then Pelayia was there, and within a few minutes Tara was standing in a massive, high-ceilinged room decorated in white and gold. The curtains were sun-gold in colour, with matching bedspread and carpet. The velvet headboard and furniture were upholstered in leaf-green; all the walls were white. The whole aspect was delightful to the eye, giving an impression of good taste characterised by restraint. In the bathroom she had found thick silky towels, bath foam and talc—everything a woman would want—and she wondered how many women Leon had brought here to stay with him.

Her eyes strayed, slowly, reluctantly, to the door between this room and the one beyond. She listened for a sound, but apparently her husband was not in there—of if he was he made so sound. A sigh that was almost a sob rose from the very heart of her. To be imprisoned like this, yearning for the man she loved but forced to endure the attentions of her abductor!

Endure.... It was dishonest to pretend that she did not enjoy Leon's lovemaking. He drew her by some powerful force, tempted her by his subtle approach and conquered her by his mastery. What kind of a woman was she? So many times since she had met this foreigner who was now her husband she had asked herself this question. Once she had been shy, avoiding any man who might prove to be too amorous for her. David had come along and she had known from the first that he was the one for her.

And yet she could enjoy the savage pagan lovemaking of another man....

It was all too baffling for her, and in any case she found herself stiffening and staring with widening eyes at the handle of the communicating door. It was turning, slowly, silently. The man was not human, she thought, managing to do things as silently as he. But the door was locked and he had to use the key.

He entered the room and Tara found herself swinging around, hoping that Pelayia was still there. But the maid had gone, for as yet there was nothing to unpack, the suitcases which Leon had bought for her and filled not yet having been brought upstairs.

Leon stood in the doorway, the light from behind him throwing his features into shade so that he appeared more satanic than ever. She frowningly examined the taut lines of his face, the tensed muscles of his neck, the hollows in his cheeks and the low forehead of the Greek, lined and darkly evil. A formidable

enemy! And yet from some hidden recess strength came
to her. She would fight him with everything in her!
Why should she succumb meekly as she had been doing?

'Come here,' he commanded, pointing to a place near
his feet.

'I'm looking at the view,' she snapped, taking a sideways step that brought her closer to the window across
which the curtains had not been drawn.

'In the dark?' with a satirical lift of his brows. 'Don't
be absurd——'

'I can see,' she interrupted. 'I'm not blind.'

'Well, you'll not see much in the dark—the lights on
the cliffs, of course, and the sea.'

'What do you want?' she demanded, taking another
step towards the window.

'I've told you to come here! If you had any sense at
all, Tara, you'd have learned by now that I am not the
man to brook defiance. Obey me—at once!'

She swallowed convulsively, aware of his intentions.
He wanted to kiss her, to caress her body, to use his vast
experience and finesse to triumph over her resistance.
He had done it every night since their marriage, laughing with satisfaction at his victory, had taunted with
the declaration that she desired him as much as he desired her. And that was why he was so confident that
she would very soon abandon her attempt to find a
way of escape. Even if a child were not on the way he
meant to hold her prisoner, not by force but by the
weakness of her resistance to his charms as a lover. And
she had to admit that she was frightened—of herself
as much as him. He was looking at her warningly and
she said, playing for time,

'Where are my clothes? I want to wash and change.'

'Your clothes are coming.' He pointed to the spot at
his feet. 'Come to me—now!'

Her heart began to throb in wild disorder. She shook

her head and yet found herself advancing towards him.

'I—you——'

'Thank your lucky stars that you decided to obey me,' he said harshly. 'I was about to give you something to remember!'

'You'd use violence on me?'

'I intend to bring you to heel, and to keep you there!'

He reached out, gripping her wrist and jerking her trembling body to him. She felt the slight pain of the sharp contact with his body, but it was nothing to the sheer ruthlessness of his mouth as it captured hers, sensuously exploring, subduing her efforts to keep her mouth closed against the insistence of his lips. She tried to struggle, but with a laugh he vanquished her puny attempt by imprisoning both her hands in one of his, then forcing them behind her back.

'What are you going to do now?' he taunted, obviously enjoying her helplessness and the white-hot fury that resulted from it. She just managed to say, 'I wish I could kill you,' before his hard mouth crushed out the rest. 'Wildcat that you are,' he mocked, 'you're not going to take very much taming.' His hand released hers and stole to her breast, to caress it with the sort of rough persuasion which he knew would fire her emotions. And it did, setting every nerve in her body rioting. How easily this hateful foreigner could arouse her all-consuming desire for the pleasure and the pain of his body! It infuriated her that he was so fully aware of his power over her, his ability to bring about her surrender. Despairingly she felt herself going limp in his arms, then arching her body as she began to strain it to his. This was defeat! It brought tears of anger to her eyes even as she continued to strain against him, vitally aware that she herself was tempting now, and that, within seconds, she would be swept unresistingly into the vortex of his passion.

# CHAPTER SEVEN

TARA stood by the fountain, staring out over the olive-clad slopes to the aquamarine sea of Greece and the sharply-defined line of the horizon beyond. She was fully conscious of the two gardeners working on the borders, and when a few minutes later her husband appeared from the house she turned on him, viciously declaring she would escape in spite of the fact that she was watched whenever she strayed from the house.

'Don't be such a vixen,' he drawled, a frown touching his brow. 'I can see I shall have to school you in the end.'

'Threats again?' She shrugged her shoulders in a gesture of indifference. 'I'm used to them by now. I've been married to you for three weeks, remember.'

His dark eyes scrutinised her flushed face. Then they narrowed, glintingly.

'You're the most stubborn woman I've ever met,' he told her at length.

'Because I haven't fallen victim to your—er—charms?' He said nothing and she added tauntingly, 'What a blow to your ego it must be to find a woman who hasn't fallen in love with you. How many hearts have you broken in your life?' she asked finally.

'You have fallen victim to my——' He stopped and the dark frown became more pronounced. 'From the first, desire has been there. You must have admitted to yourself many times that, physically, I can give you far more than that David you talk about.' He watched her closely and anger throbbed at the knowledge that he knew she would not be able truthfully to argue with his statement.

'But I haven't fallen in love with you,' she said defensively.

'Not yet, but there is plenty of time.'

'Is it important to you that I fall in love with you?'

He shrugged his shoulders.

'Not really. Life would be more pleasant if you did, for then you wouldn't be such a termagant.'

She gritted her teeth.

'I was never like this till I met you!'

'Obviously not, because no one would ever have fallen in love with you.' A pause and then, 'This David's had a narrow escape, if he only knew it.'

Tara drew a breath, and managed to control the fury within her. She had several times made the resolve to be calm—icily calm—hoping that such an attitude would successfully attack *his* calm. But she kept losing control and showing him her temper. He had shaken her on two occasions, and on several more had threatened her with a beating. But he had never lost control to that extent; she felt that he was always conscious of preserving his dignity, and he did preserve it for most of the time. She glanced at the two gardeners, a brooding expression on her face. Would there ever be an opportunity of escape? She thought of her husband's need to attend to his various businesses and wondered when he would be going to Athens. He would not take her with him, he had said, and of course the reason was his inability to keep her a prisoner there, as he could so easily do on this small island where she was watched every minute of every day.

He glanced at her, his eyes following the direction of her gaze.

'How transparent you are,' he mocked. 'Don't you ever stop thinking of getting away from me?'

'No, never,' she flashed back at him. 'I could almost wish those two would drop dead!'

'If you did leave me,' commented her husband

mildly, 'just look what you would miss.' He was taunting her as usual, reminding her of her weakness.

'You pompous ass!' It was out before she realised it,
and she knew for sure that it was only the presence of
the gardeners that saved her from punishment. As it
was, Leon's black eyes glittered with fury and his mouth
went tight.

'By God, girl, you're asking for it! If I don't take a
stick to you before long it will be a miracle!' The eyes
smouldered now, and Tara saw his hands clench as if
their owner would like to have her throat within their
grip. She shivered and resolved to be more careful in
future.

'I hate your repeated references to your prowess as
a—as a—lover,' she muttered, amazed at her own words
but aware that they were spoken in order to break the
awful silence that had dropped between them.

'Because they remind you that I never fail to make
you surrender?' He was his cool suave self again, his
expression one of sardonic amusement. 'Deep down,
you wanted to be married to me——'

'You forced me into marriage! Oh, how can you say
that I *wanted* to marry you? I'm in love with someone
else!'

'No, you are not,' he stated firmly. 'If you were then
how could you enjoy lying in another man's arms?'

She bent her head, embarrassment staining her
cheeks a vivid crimson.

'It's only—only in *that* way——' She stopped, her
head still bent, and, with a thread of laughter in his
tone he finished for her,

'——that you are attracted to me.'

She lifted her face, to see him regarding her with a
faintly sardonic smile in his eyes.

'One day,' she whispered, 'I shall be free of this—
this attraction you speak of.'

'You will never be free ... will you?' he challenged,

watching her through narrowed eyes. 'I knew when I saw you in that hospital ward that fate had given you into my keeping—for ever.' He took her hand, staring down at the ring she wore. 'Will you ever be free?' he asked again, and it was as if some force beyond her control compelled her to answer as he desired she should answer.

'No,' she quivered with a long-drawn-out sigh that was very like a sob, for it came from the very core of her heart. 'I will never be free, Leon.'

'Sensible girl to admit it. Perhaps you will now settle down and accept the good life that is offered to you.'

She looked at him through a mist of tears.

'I have no life. You've robbed me of all happiness, both now and in the future.'

His hands closed tightly again, but she sensed that the cause was not anger this time, but rather the outward sign of some tumultuous emotion inwardly affecting him. A nerve in his throat pulsated, fascinating her as she stared at it. Then her eyes moved, to notice the sunlight on his temple, turning the grey hairs to silver. He had told her he was thirty-one, but he looked older—perhaps the result of the dissolute life he led, she thought.

He turned to glance at her and for a moment fixed his gaze on her eyes, and the brightness he saw there. A frown knit his brow; he seemed about to speak but changed his mind, and then, his face harsh in the sunlight, he walked away, leaving her standing there, desolate and alone, and yet the curious pain which pierced her heart seemed not to be anything to do with her own plight, but rather to be for the man whose unwilling prisoner she was.

After a while she began to wander in the grounds; the gardener who had been busy weeding the border at the end of one of the lawns moved slowly, casually a garden fork in his hand. With the other hand he took

a string of worry beads from his pocket and began
clicking them; she heard faintly a low masculine
sound, as though he were singing or humming a tune
to himself. A sigh escaped her. She had told her husband she would never be free, but already she was
thinking of freedom. In his presence she seemed to be
hypnotised by him, submitting to his wishes like a puppet on a string, and she had often wondered if he would
in the end captivate her totally by a combination of
mastery and the lovemaking which always transported
her to the supreme height of bliss. Undoubtedly she was
getting something out of marriage to him—and he was
fully aware of it. She was putty in his hands when he
had her emotions heightened; she responded in every
way to his demands, surrender bringing its own fulfilment.

And at those times she never even thought of David,
or the tragedy of her wedding day. He was a nebulous
figure who had flitted through her life and was no
longer important. But in the cold light of day when she
was free of the fascination and domination of her husband, she did think of David, and the home they had
got together—the furniture bought with such care, the
carpets and curtains, all purchased after long and
happy interludes of discussion as to colour schemes and
durability. It had been such fun, during those months
of preparation, she recalled nostalgically. She and her
fiancé had wandered hand in hand through the shops,
each thinking of the great day when they would be together in the cosy little home they were building.

And now.... Would she and David ever come together again, after she had managed to escape? There
would have to be a divorce first ... and Greek men did
not believe in divorce.... And suppose there was a
child? No, she whispered vehemently. No, there must
not be a child! Leon had been so confident, though,
that a child would arrive quite soon. For her, that

would be the end of hopes for escape——

'I won't think about it!' she whispered fiercely to herself. 'I must think about getting away, because the longer I stay the more likely I am to become pregnant!'

That evening at dinner she was very quiet, her mind fixed on the problem of getting away. Leon, taking it for granted that she was abstracted for another reason altogether, frowned darkly at her and snapped,

'It's time you got that fellow out of your system! You're my wife now and the sooner you resign yourself to it the better!'

The scowl on his face marred an effect which—Tara grudgingly admitted—could have been incredibly attractive. For Leon, immaculate in an oyster-white linen suit with a pastel-green shirt, had that particular air of distinction found only among the nobility. He gave the impression always of a cultured gentleman of rather special lineage, and as if that were not enough he possessed the added attributes of good looks and physical perfection, his tall lithe frame—like that of an athlete in perfect form—carrying not one ounce of excess weight.

He was still glowering at her and she returned quietly,

'I shall never get David out of my system. He's the man I chose for a husband, the one I knew I could love, and be happy with, for the rest of my life.'

'You would not have been happy!' Imperious the tone, and challenging. Tara's intention of arguing with his statement died on her lips. 'I give you so much! Why can't you be satisfied?'

'There should be love in marriage—that's why I'm not satisfied!'

He drew a breath of impatience.

'You English are so damned sentimental—especially the women. Tell me, how long does this so-called love last?'

'It can last for ever, but you as a Greek wouldn't understand. Loving and caring are the most important part of marriage.'

'The physical compatibility? Is that not important?'

'In a way ... yes——'

'In a way?' His straight black brows lifted a fraction. 'Can you honestly tell me that physical compatibility's not the most important thing in our marriage?'

'It's the only thing in our marriage.'

'What about the material aspect? Most women would be more than happy with what you have—or can have when I'm sure you'll not try to run from me. I can give you every luxury—we have a rather special home here, you must admit? We have a yacht, and when eventually you come with me to Athens you'll live in a luxury flat and have your own car.'

'All those, but not love.'

'Tell me,' he said, 'how many of your friends—who presumably married for love—are as idyllically happy as you appear to believe possible?'

She looked at him but said nothing. She was remembering Sue one day rattling off all the couples they knew whose marriages were broken, or about to be. It was frightening, Sue had said, and Tara remembered saying that she and David were lucky because they both knew that their love would last for ever.

'Well,' challenged Leon, breaking into her thoughts, 'what answer have you for me?'

She gave an audible sigh and shook her head.

'Love can last,' she said doggedly.

'But you can't think of any of your friends who are happily married?' A sort of smooth satire edged his accented voice and his eyes held amusement. 'Here in Greece we have the answer, no matter what you say to the contrary. We marry for physical satisfaction and the production of children. Marriages in the villages are still arranged by parents, who know better than their children what is good for them——'

'Stop! It's—horrible to think of arranged marriages!'

'Forget love,' he advised, ignoring the interruption, 'and be satisfied with what you have. When you stop having these vixenish turns you and I will be very happy indeed.'

'I've just remembered that you expressed the wish that I would fall in love with you.'

'I said life would be more pleasant if you did, but by "love" I didn't mean some grand passion—the sort some writers are carried away with. To me there is no such grand passion—unless it's a physical one,' he added with a hint of amusement. 'But this deep love one hears about——' He shrugged it off impatiently. 'It's nothing but nonsense.'

'You're going to miss a lot in life,' she stated. But then she added, 'However, I daresay you'll satisfy yourself with more sensual pleasures.'

'You're a little bitch, Tara,' he said softly. 'I wonder how long I shall be able to accept your poisonous barbs without retaliation.'

Tara said nothing and for a while they ate in silence. But although her husband did not speak there was no mistaking the interest he was taking in her appearance. She had acquired a lovely golden-sienna tan from lying out in the sun, and her hair had become bleached at the same time, especially at the front where it crowned her high intelligent forehead. Her eyes were wide and sad, and now and then her mouth would tremble convulsively, the result of her thoughts. She looked very young and defenceless to the man sitting opposite, and whose eyes were fixed upon her with the most odd expression in their depths. She saw the hint of a frown touch his forehead momentarily. He seemed to become lost in thought and the frown reappeared.

'I'll give a small dinner-party next week,' he decided

suddenly. 'It's time I began showing my beautiful wife off.'

'I could enlist their help!' She stared at him in surprise. 'Are you willing to take the risk?'

'My dear child, can you imagine my friends listening to your saying you were kidnapped and forced into marriage, and believing it? They'd think you were a little mad.'

Her teeth clenched together. He was right, of course, as he always was! How she hated him! He seemed so confident that she could not escape ... but one day she would show him!

Several days before the dinner party Leon bought a dress for Tara which he put on the bed. She asked where he had got it, suspecting for one revolted moment that it was one left behind by one of his women friends. Her face obviously revealed her suspicions, because Leon said laughingly,

'I wouldn't do a thing like that to my wife, Tara. To one of the others, yes, but never to you.'

'You respect me?' she challenged with a curious glance.

There was a pause, as if he were not sure about voicing the answer that was on his lips. However, he did voice it, but spoke quickly and offhandedly.

'More than I've ever respected a woman before.' He gestured to the dress and added before she had time to speak, 'It's the same size as the others. I bought it in the village here.'

'The village?' she echoed, puckering her forehead. 'Is there a dress shop in the village?'

'There's a dressmaker—Margarita. She made it to my design.' He looked at her, smiling at her expression of surprise. 'I shall allow you to go down to the village when I have your promise that you won't run away.'

'I shall never make a promise like that——' She

stopped, and stared at him, wide-eyed. 'You would trust me—if I did give you the promise?' Her heart was pounding against her ribs. To make the promise would result in freedom ... and the chance of getting off this island. ... Ferry boats were plying to and from Piraeus all the time; she could see them from the terrace.

The shrewd dark eyes narrowed as Leon read her mind.

'If you made me that promise, Tara, you would keep it.'

She frowned in puzzlement.

'What do you mean?'

'I trust you,' he answered simply.

'You trust me—to that extent?' She shook her head disbelievingly. 'You wouldn't be such a fool.'

'You would not let me down,' he said confidently. 'I'd be more than willing to give you your freedom if you made me the promise I've asked for.'

She said nothing, her mind in turmoil. He would trust her! It seemed impossible that he would do so. Surely he could see that there would be nothing dishonourable in her giving him the promise and then breaking it. She had every right to break it—and she would!

Or would she ...?

'Well?' prompted her husband softly.

She looked at him and shook her head.

'No,' she decided reluctantly, 'I can't give you the promise.'

'Later, perhaps,' he said casually, and reverted to the subject of the dressmaker. 'Margarita has a small establishment at the end of the harbour. She's a wizard with the needle. I'm seriously considering bringing her into the firm.' There was a strange pause then, before Leon added, 'You will meet Elene at the dinner party; she's the most beautiful and talented of all our models.'

'Oh....' For apparently no reason at all a sudden

chill fluttered along Tara's back. 'She's Greek?'

'Her father's Greek and her mother's English.' Leon idly picked up the dress, fingering the beautifully-embroidered material with the touch of the expert. Tara was fascinated, for this man was so very different from the arrogant, forbidding one she knew so well. He glanced from the dress to his wife's slender figure, and then he was examining her face, and her hair.

'I ought to have had your hair cut before now,' he frowned. 'Remind me to phone for the hairdresser to come up here tomorrow.'

Tara's eyes blazed.

'I shall do no such thing! I happen to like my hair as it is!'

He shook his head, her anger having made not the slightest impression on him as he said,

'It doesn't suit you—not for the way I intend to dress you. Certainly it won't go with this particular evening gown.'

'The way *you* intend to dress *me*!' she gasped. 'What do you think I am—a spineless slave whose function in life is to obey and please her master! You can think again,' she added in a suffocated voice, 'because I've no intention of being told what I shall wear.'

'What a wildcat you are,' he commented mildly. 'You've worn what I've provided up till now.'

'Only because I've had no choice.'

'You'll always wear what I choose,' he told her inexorably. 'However, when I have that promise I asked for you will be able to come to Athens with me and look around the shops.'

She would always wear what he chose! Fury scorched her cheeks, but by a tremendous effort she managed to curb her tongue.

But she resolved not to wear the dress he had provided.

The night of the dinner party arrived, and after shower-
ing and drying herself Tara slipped into a négligé and
picked up the dress which she had earlier chosen from
the wardrobe. But she went and looked at the other
and had to admit that it was sheer perfection. Carna-
tion pink in colour, it had an underslip of pampas
green which showed through the open pattern of the
embroidery. The neck was low, the bodice cut to
accentuate her curves. The sleeves were long, cut from
the waist in enormous folds. She had tried it on that
morning, after her hair had been cut, and in spite of
herself she had weakened, half deciding that she would
wear it after all, for nothing could have made her look
lovelier. Leon certainly had the kind of flair that brings
success to any fashion house.

'I shan't wear it!' she said determinedly, and went
over to where the other one lay over the back of a chair.
'He's not going to dictate to me!'

She was standing before the dressing-table when
Leon came from the other room, looking superb in a
pale green linen suit and white frilled shirt. He took
one step and then stopped, his eyes fixed disbelievingly
on her figure.

'What's happened?' he demanded. 'Is something
wrong with the dress——'

'Nothing's wrong with it,' she broke in, infuriated
at the knowledge that her heart was beating far too
quickly. 'I'm not wearing it, that's all. I like this one
better,' she lied, touching the front with her finger.

'You——!' He strode across the room and stood over
her, a tall menacing figure, his face black as thunder.
'Get out of that at once! It's not an evening gown——'

'I know it isn't! I do have some dress sense!'

'Where's the other?' he wanted to know, his voice
quieter now but vibrating with anger.

'In the wardrobe.' She swallowed convulsively, mili-
tant even while she trembled. 'I'm not wearing it.'

'By God you are!' His black eyes smouldered as he added, 'Do you get this one off or do I?'

She backed away, her cheeks draining of colour.

'Don't you dare touch me,' she faltered, terrified that he was going to hit her. 'I——' the rest was cut as, with a strong sweep of his hand, he ripped the dress from neck almost to hem. And before she could move he had stripped it from her, leaving her standing there in her undies and tights. 'Go and get the other!' He pointed imperiously to the wardrobe. 'Get it, Tara, or else.' Fury swept over her like a deluge, but she obeyed him for all that, aware as she was of her scanty attire— so little covering if he should be driven by his anger to beat her.

'I don't w-want to—to wear it,' she quivered, holding it in her hand.

'Put it on.'

Again she obeyed, tears of anger sparkling on her lashes.

'That's better. Our guests will be here in a few minutes, so don't be long.' And with that he strode towards the door again and disappeared through it.

'I hate him—oh, I could kill him!' She put her face in her hands and wept bitterly into them. 'How can I go on! How can I? David ... if only I could send you a message....' The tears came again, but fear of her husband brought control and she bathed her eyes. She looked awful! And the dress, lovely as it was, had been designed by Leon to bring out every curve of her body, for even the skirt accentuated her thighs as she walked. Fury rose again, affecting both her brain and her caution. She would *not* wear it! And this time he would not be able to make her! With fumbling fingers she took it off and then, after attempting frenziedly to tear the seams apart, she went over to the dressing-table and, taking up the nail scissors, she began to cut and slash at the material.

She was in the négligé when Leon came into the room again.

'Aren't you ready yet——' This time his face twisted almost with pain as, staring at the mutilated gown, he shook his head in disbelief. Tara, uncaring now what he did to her, snatched it up and flung it in his face.

'I said I wasn't wearing it and I meant it! I shall wear *what I choose*—get that!'

He was inflamed within seconds; the blood raced through his veins, creating drifts of dark crimson at the sides of his mouth. With the agility of a jungle cat he leapt the distance between them and the next moment the blood was pounding in Tara's head as he shook her with prolonged and savage intensity, shook her until he himself was out of breath. The négligé had come open; it slipped from her shoulders and once more she was standing before him, half naked.

'What the hell are you going to wear now? You've nothing suitable!' She heard the gritting of his teeth, saw him glance at the watch on his wrist. And in spite of the fact that she was almost in a state of collapse, she knew the thrill of having won her first victory over him.

He was at the wardrobe, looking along the rail. Tara waited, conscious of the silence in the room, and of the only sound outside being that of the cicadas making their nocturnal chant in the olive trees. He turned at last, a turquoise blue evening gown in his hand. To Tara, it was charming, but to him it obviously was not up to the standard he had required for this particular evening when he was having guests.

'This will have to do. Put it on.'

She obeyed, all the fight gone out of her. But she was still enjoying a certain amount of exultation at the idea of what she had done. It would perhaps convince her husband that she was not totally subservient to his will.

# CHAPTER EIGHT

THE front door was being opened as Tara came down from the bedroom. Leon had already welcomed a couple of guests, and he was now in the hall as Stamati, having stood aside to allow a young man and a girl to enter, closed the door and took the mink wrap which the girl handed to him. Tara stared, gasping at the flawless beauty of the girl who, she knew instinctively, was the model of whom her husband had spoken. Tall and poised and charmingly attired in a gown of sheer perfection designed to show off to every advantage the lovely curves of her body, she was the epitome of feminine supremacy. Tara, glancing down at her own dress, would have liked to turn and run, so inferior did she feel. The other dress had been beautiful, a model designed by her husband to enhance all the beauty of face and figure which he evidently saw in her. She could now understand his feelings; she could not understand her own in deliberately destroying what had been expertly designed and produced especially for her.

She noticed the glinting expression in Leon's face as, fleetingly, his eyes swept from the delightful picture of his model to the figure of his wife.

'Elene,' he said coolly, 'meet my wife, Tara.'

The girl extended a hand, her dark eyes flickering over Tara's dress. Whatever her thoughts were it was impossible to say. She was a girl who gave nothing away —at least, not by her expression.

Tara took the hand, aware of an icy chill enveloping her whole frame, for there seemed to be hostility hidden in the girl's manner, an underlying hatred, even.

'How do you do?' Elene turned immediately to Leon.

'How charming! And what a surprise for us all! I could scarcely believe you when you phoned to tell me the news.'

The ghost of a smile was all the response Leon made to that. He introduced his wife to the young man, Nico Kallergis, Elene's escort for the evening. Of medium height, with jet black hair and dark brown eyes, he was handsome in a thick-set kind of way. At twenty-eight he was the owner of two cruise ships and extensive olive groves on the mainland of Greece. He took Tara's hand and held it rather longer than was necessary. She met his gaze and an unfathomable sensation filtered through her. There was friendliness in his stare, and in the smile that curved his full mouth.

'Happy to meet you, Tara,' he said sincerely, his eyes darting to Elene and then to Leon. 'How did you manage to pierce the armour of our most confirmed bachelor?'

She coloured but offered no reply, profoundly conscious of Elene's supercilious glance which seemed to say that Leon had not married her for her smartness and good taste.

Tara was in fact inwardly squirming, conscious of the fact that her husband was the head of one of the top fashion houses of the world. Elene must be very puzzled that Leon had not seen that his wife was better turned out than this.

Another couple arrived five minutes later and were shown into the sitting-room where Leon and his wife and guests were drinking aperitifs. This couple were married, and much older than Elene and Nico. Tara liked them well enough—as she liked the other couple, Julia and Cristakis Mitas—but she felt disinclined to chat and was content to sit and listen to the conversation going on around her. The latest couple to arrive were Agni and Loukis Amaxis, and Agni, about forty-five years of age, had obviously never been anything other than her husband's equal. Tara wondered how she had managed to lift herself to that status in a country where, traditionally, women were regarded as inferior.

'This is a sensation indeed,' Loukis had declared when on being introduced to Tara he had smiled into her eyes. 'Leon married—and never a word to any of his friends.' His accent, like that of his wife, was most noticeable—very different from those of Elene and Leon, both of whom spoke immaculate English. Agni asked if Leon and Tara had known one another long, and Tara could not help but notice that as she spoke the woman's eyes slid to the lovely girl who was sitting, a little apart from everyone else, on a chair by the window, with the deep gold curtains forming a suitable backcloth for her dark, exotic beauty.

'Not very long at all,' said Leon smoothly in reply to Agni's question. 'It was one of those instances of mutual attraction at the very first meeting.' He paused a moment to look at his wife, whose blue eyes had narrowed as she listened to words that were not in any way true. *He* might have been attracted—he *was* attracted—but she had disliked him on sight. 'And so,' continued Leon suavely, 'there was only one thing for us to do—get married.'

Elene's mouth seemed to compress. She leant forward in her chair, flicked back the lid of a gold cigarette box with the familiar touch that told Tara she had done it many times before, and took out a cigarette. Leon rose at once to pick up the matching lighter, flick it and hold it to the tip of Elene's cigarette. Tara saw their eyes meet and hold, but there was nothing to be read from the expression of either of them.

The dinner party had gone off very well, with Nico, sitting opposite to Tara, frequently monopolising her, oblivious of the dark glances cast at him by his host. Although Tara was well aware of them she remained indifferent, continuing to chat with Nico, whom she liked best of all the six guests. By the time the evening was over a bond had been cemented between them although, at this early stage in their relationship, it was merely a vague idea with them both. Yet Tara knew they would meet again ... and without others being present. ...

Just as she had anticipated, Leon's temper was high and the moment they were alone he demanded to know why she had allowed herself to be monopolised by Nico. Tara's thoughts went immediately to Elene, who had monopolised Leon on several occasions, flirting with him, showing off her beauty, and by other subtle tricks at which she seemed adept, she had made him conscious of the difference in her appearance from that of his wife. Tara's blood had boiled even though she had no idea why. Certainly she was not jealous of the camaraderie existing between Leon and his lovely model.

'I was sociable, as you expected me to be,' answered Tara shortly.

'I expected you to be sociable with the others as well!' The black eyes smouldered as they looked into hers. 'But you had no time for anyone but Nico!'

'Can I ever do anything right for you?' she demanded. 'Let me know if I ever do! I'll chalk it up——'

'Careful,' warned her husband softly. 'I'm not in the best of moods as it is.'

'Nico was pleasant to talk to,' she said. 'Certainly more pleasant than your friend Elene.' She watched his face intently for any change of expression, but she saw only an unreadable mask which told her nothing.

'You didn't care for Elene?' he queried with an odd expression in his voice. 'No, I didn't. She treated me as an inferior.'

'Because of your dress——'

'Which you bought for me!'

'Not for an occasion like tonight,' he snapped. 'A gown has to suit an occasion, and this you will have to learn.'

'Rubbish! One should wear what appeals to one.'

'You, as my wife, have to set an example. It will be expected that you will wear clothes which are correct —and that takes in style, colour and cut.'

'The expert talking! I was just a working girl until you brought me to this environment—which I hate!'

'Liar,' was his smooth and brief rejoinder. How cool and collected he appeared now! Tara had to admire the way he could control his anger and wished she was equally adept.

'I think I'll go to bed,' she decided, then flushed to the roots of her hair as Leon said,

'That's the kind of eagerness I like.'

Her teeth gritted audibly.

'I'd rather be alone—for once!'

'Liar,' he murmured again, and before she could step back he had her in his arms, tilting her face, claiming her lips with his own. 'Yes,' he said after a long while, 'it is time we went to bed.'

In the bedroom Tara stood by the window, staring broodingly out to the dark line of the horizon. Over there was her home—England and David.... Her thoughts wandered and she was recalling something Elene had said when, after dinner, the two girls found themselves together on the couch.

'No one ever expected Leon to get married in a rush like he did. It's to be hoped he won't regret it.'

It was outspoken to say the least, but, strangely, it left Tara unaffected. Elene had obviously been far more than Leon's top model; she had been his pillow-friend. She recalled the others at the dinner party, and the way they had treated her. They had been friendly enough, but seemed to wonder what Leon had seen in

the English girl who had become his wife so unexpectedly.

Nico, on the other hand, had taken to Tara right
from the start. And now, as her mind strayed to him,
his name seemed inextricably to be linked with escape.
He had a powerful motor launch, he had said, and it
was at present moored in the harbour down there.

She looked at the conglomeration of boats, some with
lights flickering in the darkness, and wondered which
one was his, and if it would one day carry her to freedom. There were several luxury craft down there, including her husband's yacht. But most of the boats were
the attractive little fishing caiques bobbing about on
the dark mirror of the sea. The moon had been up but
clouds had drifted over it, swirling drapery which
allowed moonglow to escape now and then, to throw
an enchanting and mysterious mosaic of light and shade
over the waterfront and the steep and rocky hills rising
from it. Paradise Isle, this piece of rock was called by
the natives, and it was indeed a beautiful island. Tara
opened the window, and into the room filtered exotic
perfumes from the garden and the extensive grounds
beyond it. The scent of pines on the hillside pervaded
the air one moment, the delicious perfume of roses the
next.

Suddenly Tara felt herself to be poised in the infinity
of space where nothing was real or tangible. David did
not exist; escape meant nothing and neither past nor
future was any longer important. The feeling persisted,
then she felt another presence and swung around to
find her husband standing not three feet from her, his
face dark and handsome, the front of his dressing-gown
open to reveal the absence of a pyjama coat. She
coloured when he said, breaking a silence that had been
for her a sort of magic spell,

'Not ready for me, wife?'

She sighed and shook her head, but when he drew her

to him she responded immediately to his kisses.

'Do you still maintain that you want to be alone to-night?' he asked, regarding her dark and dreamy eyes with an air of mocking amusement. She hated his expression, hated her own weakness, born of the magnetic power which he so easily exerted over her. She was as putty in his hands and the galling thing was that he knew it. He could do what he liked with her, using a mastery against which she had no defence. 'Answer me, Tara!' he insisted, his hand straying with possessive arrogance to the soft curve of a breast.

A great shuddering sigh escaped her; she lifted her face to his and answered huskily,

'No, Leon . . . I d-don't want to b-be alone. . . .'

His laugh was triumphant, his manner that of the conqueror as, bringing her close, he unzipped the evening gown and let it fall to the floor. Her face flamed as he occupied himself with the scanty coverings that were left. He had done all this before, he reminded her, so what was she blushing for? He derived amusement from her embarrassment, and she knew that he was taking his time purely for the sake of prolonging that amusement. Naked, she was in his arms, her soft breasts crushed hurtfully against the iron-hardness of his chest. His hands strayed, and then she was swung right off her feet. He held her for a space without moving, his eyes dark with the smouldering passion within him, burning into hers with fierce intensity. Her body quivered in his arms; she attempted to wrench her eyes from that masterful, compelling gaze, but she failed. His arms became stronger around her soft and supple body, drawing her more closely to him, and she felt the hard muscles of his chest and shoulders against her.

'I wonder if your struggles are now ended.' Leon's mouth was close to her temple, his fingers moving on her naked body. 'I feel sure that you've come to the point where you know it's useless to set your will against mine?'

She swallowed convulsively but made no answer. He laid her down on the bed, then stood over her, a towering figure whose primitive, pagan desires were written unmistakably on his arrogant face.

She turned away from those fierce dark eyes, but within seconds she felt his body beside her, was drawn into the inflexible steel hawser of his embrace. Every nerve, every fibre of her being was affected as his fiery kisses were rained on her lips, her throat, and lower to where a hand was laid upon her breast. She responded, straining her body to the virile mastery of his. She heard him laugh softly with triumph as all her control collapsed in the whirlpool of his ardour.

What was happening to her? she was asking herself several days later when, on being ordered by her husband to wear the new bikini he had bought, she meekly did as she was told. Was being a captive becoming a habit of mind? And was it a habit which would grow and strengthen to the point where it would be impossible to throw it off? Leon's powerful attraction for her was freely admitted, not only to herself but to Leon too, when he forced from her lips words she would never have uttered in the cold light of day. But he knew when to coerce her, and how to bring her to the depth of being nothing more than his meek and willing slave. When in the throes of passion and desperate yearning she could be compelled without much trouble to obey every command she was given. She wondered if he knew that she was still afraid of him, of his strength and his imperious manner when he was issuing orders—as today when he had told her to wear the bikini—and of the threat in his eyes when they darkened. She thought of her struggles, which had merely given her bruises—before she suffered total defeat.

Even from the first she had known that her puny strength would never be a match for his, but yet her instinct had made her fight him. Now, though, she was coming to the point where she was resigned to her situation. Yes, undoubtedly she was becoming resigned, and she asked herself again if being her husband's captive was becoming a habit of mind. ·

He made her don the bikini in front of him; it was a domineering retaliation for the frowning way she had looked at it, as there was scarcely anything of it at all!

He had obviously liked it, she thought, and in fact he had nodded with satisfaction when she stood there before him.

'Go into the garden,' he said, but added that she must not get too much sun at one time.

'Are you coming?' She hoped he would say no, as she loved to be alone in the garden because there, in the warmth of the sun and the peace of her surroundings, she could relax both in mind and in body. The sensation of tranquillity and aloneness was balm to the ache of remembrance. She seemed able to forget David and the tragedy and horror of her wedding day, when she had been ruthlessly snatched by the pagan Greek who had forced her into marriage. Very early it had hit her that he had had no need to marry her, that he could have taken her as his mistress—in which case, he would have been free to cast her off just whenever he tired of her. Why, then, had he married her?

His alien voice broke into her reflections as he said he would not be keeping her company in the garden yet awhile as he had work to do in his study. She looked at him, profoundly conscious of those black eyes, roving, taking in for their owner's erotic pleasure every curve of her near-naked body. He had told her several times that he owned her body and therefore he could do what he liked with it, and she wondered as she tried to read his expression if he were thinking that now, at this moment. She quivered, looking around for the beach wrap he had bought her. She was in no mood for making love at this time of day!

'What are you looking for?' he wanted to know, reaching for her hand and pulling her gently towards him.

'My wrap—please let me get it. I think it's in the bathroom.' She had no idea where it was; she wanted only to get away from him. But Leon had other ideas and it was not until he had satiated his desire that he allowed her to go and get the wrap, and had told her again to go into the garden.

She lay back on the lounger listening to the droning of insects in the flower borders and watching one of the gardeners as he kept an eye on her, glancing her way now and then, just to make sure she had not got up and run off—clad in nothing more than the bikini and the very short wrap which Leon had bought along with it!

She had been lying there for about an hour when she was awakened from her soporific state by the voice of her husband.

'You look good enough to eat,' he commented with the kind of smile she had never seen on his face before. 'Shall I join you?'

'I can't stop you,' she replied, flicking a hand to the other lounger a couple of feet away.

'Don't be bitchy,' he snapped, the smile fading, and replaced by a frown. 'I'm obviously not wanted,' he added as he sat down. He was dressed in shorts, and a T-shirt which accentuated the muscles of his arms and shoulders. Undoubtedly he had an air of distinction even in these clothes, Tara admitted grudgingly. Her eyes wandered to his face with its teak-bronzed skin, its arrogant features and strong, classical jawline. His mouth was not so thin as usual, and its sensuality was more apparent. She found herself comparing him with David—as she had one once or twice before—and decided that there really was no comparison: you didn't compare a tiger with a lamb.

She said, asking the question which she knew she would ask at one time or another.

'Why did you marry me, Leon?' He merely looked at her sharply and gave her no answer. 'You had no need,' she went on, watching him intently. 'You had me in your power. If you'd—er—amused yourself without marriage, then you could have got rid of me when you found someone else.'

'That would have been impossible under the circumstances.' He was watching the gardener, his face inscrutable.

'What do you mean?'

'I abducted you, remember. If I'd taken you and then cast you off you'd have been able to have me arrested. As it is, you haven't any sort of a case against me. Marriage was my only safeguard against finding myself in trouble.'

'What do you mean—I haven't any sort of case against you?'

'You married me willingly. You're now my wife——' He threw out his hands. 'What could you do if, say, you did manage to escape?'

'I'd still go to the police.'

He shook his head.

'It would get you nowhere. You promised to marry me, remember? And you did marry me—without a word of protest, without making even the slightest accusation against me.'

'You consider yourself so clever,' she retorted, 'but I shall have my revenge one day!'

His eyes hardened.

'You are still dreaming of escape?'

'Of course.'

'Foolish girl. Hasn't it dawned on you that you are pregnant?'

Her eyes flew to his, crimson colour staining her cheeks.

'No!' she cried. 'No—how can you be sure ...?' Her voice trailed to silence as his black brows lifted.

'I wasn't born yesterday,' he said with a significant edge of satire to his voice. 'You're my prisoner now, Tara—inescapably.'

'No—I won't have your child! I don't want it! I hate you too much!' She was on the brink of tears, because his assertion had only served to strengthen the first dawning of doubt in her mind, a doubt she had cast away, desperately thrusting it from her consciousness. Fate would not do that to her! It wasn't fair! She was *not* expecting a child! The tears flowed and she reached for the wrap, seeking in the pocket for a handkerchief. Her hand came away empty and Leon gave her his. 'If you knew how much I hate you,' she quivered after she had dried her eyes, 'you'd let me go at once!'

Her husband ignored that, accepting his handkerchief from her gingerly after having seen her blow her nose on it. She looked very young, like a child, her eyes still moist, and small sobs rising to her lips. His eyes flickered over her, and it did seem that they had softened slightly. And that nerve in his neck ... it was there again, pulsating, out of control. He said after a long silence,

'If you give me that promise, Tara, then I shall allow you the freedom of this island. As it is, you're not allowed outside the grounds of the house. Be sensible, child, and give me the promise.'

'You've just said I'm your prisoner now—inescapably,' she reminded him, 'so why do you want the promise?'

'Until the child is born I'm taking no chances. I

know you well enough to be sure that you'd never desert your child. I also know you well enough to be sure
that if you give me that promise you will keep it. I've
said so before.'

She remained silent, musing on what he had said. If
she could escape before the child was born——

'I'm not having a child!' she whispered to herself
vehemently. 'It would ruin my life—David would never
want another man's child, so he would no longer want
to marry me!'

Leon was saying, changing the subject,

'I must go to Athens within the next week. I'd take
you with me if you'd give me that promise.' His eyes
had a questioning look as he waited—hopefully, it was
plain—for her to give him the answer he required. She
shook her head and said no, she would not make the
promise. 'You're the most stubborn woman I have ever
met!' he exclaimed exasperatedly. 'I *want* to take you
with me!'

'For *one thing*,' she returned with scorn. 'Can't you
look up one of your old flames and invite her to sleep
with you?'

Leon's eyes glimmered, like burning embers ready to
ignite.

'Get inside!' he ordered harshly, rising as he spoke
and jerking her up with him. 'I've had enough! You'll
feel my hand about your hide for what you've just
said!' He was dragging her, and because she was so conscious of the gardener's eyes following them, Tara re-
frained from struggling. Her heart was pounding
against her ribs, for despite the repeated threats he had
made she had felt sure he would never use violence
upon her. She thought of her scanty attire and every
drop of blood drained from her face. He would hurt
her—she had had plenty of proof of his savagery when
his temper was roused, so she could expect no mercy
now. Should she plead? Such cowardly conduct was

abhorrent to her, but not more so than the instinctive shrinking from physical punishment, especially at the hands of this fiend.

Once in the bedroom he kicked the door closed, then stood with his broad back to it, his face twisted into evil lines, his eyes blazing with fury. She had run when he released her hand and she was standing with her back to the window, an animal at bay with her merciless predator ready to spring. She suddenly knew she must plead, for all courage had been drained from her.

'Leon—please—don't hurt me!'

'Come here!' he thundered, and her heart began to beat with such violence that she felt it would collapse altogether. She put a hand to it, tears streaming down her face. He gritted his teeth and pointed to the floor in front of him. 'Here, I said. My God, girl, if you don't obey me you'll be sorry!'

'I c-can't—oh, Leon, please. . . .' He said nothing, but continued to point to the spot in front of him. The silence was torture; her forehead was clammy and so were the palms of her hands. 'I'll do anything you say——' She stopped, and although it was the most difficult thing she had ever done in the whole of her life, she humbly apologised for what she had said. The tears continued to flow, created by the terrible fear this man put into her as he stood there, his finger still pointing. Slowly she advanced, gripped in a vice of sheer terror, for he looked as if he were ready to give her more than a beating; he looked ready to murder her, And suddenly it struck her that his fury was out of all proportion. He'd admitted to having pillow-friends, so why should he be like this simply because she had mentioned them? True, he would not like it, but this. . . . She stared into his face after coming to a halt before his towering figure. He had said he respected her more than he had respected any other woman—so could it be possible that he wanted to forget those others?

Stunned by the idea, Tara continued to stare, forget-
ting that at any moment she might find herself grasped
and beaten. If he wanted to forget the others then it
meant that he—— She cut her thoughts, admitting
that it was not possible that he was beginning to like
her ... in *that* way. Hadn't he said several times that
he did not believe in love?

'So you decided to apologise, eh?' Although his voice
rasped it seemed to have lost some of its vibrancy, and
she sensed that his anger was abating. 'You saved yourself,' he said, and for a long moment she could only
stare, her shredded nerves gradually settling, along with
the painful, rapid throbbing of her heart. 'Yes, you
were wise—in fact, it is the wisest thing you have ever
done.' His black eyes roved over her body possessively;
she was jerked to him and his mouth was brutal as it
crushed hers. She fought for breath, twisting about instinctively, managing at last to draw her bruised and
swollen lips from his. He gave a snarl and forced her
head up with a merciless hand beneath her chin. 'Did I
say you'd escaped! The beating, yes—but not my
kisses!' His hand forced her head further back, until
she felt a pain in her neck. The dark head was bent, the
evil mouth caressed hers before, with the same savage
intensity, he crushed hers beneath it.

She wept softly. Unable to fight him any more, she
accepted defeat and went limp in his arms. He was the
conqueror, her master, and in this moment of pain and
despair she owned it to herself that she must never
again fight against his strength. It exhausted her, it
caused the blood to pound in her temples. Why did she
do it? The instinct of self-preservation which right
down through the ages had brought reprisals to those
whose enemies were stronger than they, and it was
bringing reprisals to her, as it always did. Pride had
made her fight, but her husband had stripped her of
all pride a moment ago when she had been forced to

apologise to him. 'I'll tame you yet,' he was saying, and now his voice was almost mild. 'The Greeks don't tolerate disobedience and ridicule, not even from men, much less from their women. You are "my woman" in this country and as such you will render me total obedience and respect.' Her head was jerked up again and she was forced to meet his fierce, compelling gaze. 'Do I make myself clear—wife!'

'Yes,' she answered, the gruffness in her voice sounding strange even to her own ears. 'Yes, Leon, you make yourself perfectly clear.'

'Good! Perhaps our lives will be lived a little more peacefully now.' His hand slid from her chin to her shoulder. The strap of her bikini bra was removed and she felt his hand curl round her breast. He was demonstrating his mastery, daring her to protest, or even to move. She dared not move, even when the other strap was released and she was naked but for the tiny covering lower down. His touch was roughly coercive; he was employing arrogant compulsion to bring her to the very depths of submission, because he knew what the fire of his touch could ignite within her, reducing her resistance to ashes. His other hand slid possessively down her spine, its progress that of slow, compelling temptation. She quivered throughout her entire body, quivered with expectation as every desire was awakened by his hands as they continued to explore. His pagan dominance was reducing her to total subjugation. He ordered her to kiss him and she obeyed, and when he laughed with taunting mockery she endured the humiliation in silence.

'You want me,' he stated, and then made her say it. Cheeks flaming, she did as she was told. His hand was removing the one scant item of clothing and she knew as before that every act was designed to bring right home to her that he was her master. Every drop of blood in her body seemed to be flooding to her heart as he lifted her, with that familiar ease that more than demonstrated his incredible muscular strength. She looked into his ruthless face as he laid her on the bed; there was triumph in his eyes, and taunting satire. He gloated at her weakness, exulted in his own strength.

And suddenly she forgot all her resolutions, even forgot her fear of him. For some power seemed to enter into her, providing her with the strength to spring off the bed and race for the communicating door. She passed through it, slamming it in his face. But in her wild fumbling with the key, which she had known was on his side of the door, she lost precious seconds. With a moan of despair she fell backwards as the door was pushed towards her. Leon caught her, miraculously, before she touched the floor, his arm a steel hawser encircling her naked body, his mouth cruel against her quivering lips. Her unexpected action had inflamed him and he showed no mercy when, a few moments later, she was his prisoner, his submissive slave.

# CHAPTER NINE

Tara was alone in the garden when Nico was announced by one of her husband's manservants. Her heart gave a little jerk; she had known instinctively that she and Nico would meet ... alone.

'He asked for *Mrs* Leon,' said Davos in an expressionless voice. 'Shall I bring him here?'

'No; show him into the sitting-room and tell him I'll be there in about five minutes.'

'Very good, madam.'

She glanced at the gardener and smiled to herself. None of the servants had been told by Leon to be present if she had a visitor, simply because he had not expected her to have one.

Excitement filled her mind as she changed quickly from the shorts and sun-top she had on, to a pleated linen dress, deep mauve with a narrow band of purple running round the hem. It was one of several that had come up from Margarita a few days ago, beautiful garments all of them, and there was silk underwear too, and a couple of blouses and skirts. She stood looking in the mirror for a moment after applying lip-rouge and perfume. Why had Nico come? As he had asked for her it was feasible to assume that he knew Leon was not at home. He rose as she entered the room, his eyes appreciative as they roved her elegantly-clad figure.

'*Yassoo*, Tara!' he greeted her, extending both his hands so that she had no option but to put hers into them. 'I knew Leon was away from home, so I decided to come and see you. Why didn't he take you with him?'

'He was going on business and I wasn't really inter-

ested,' she lied glibly as she swept a hand, inviting him
to sit down again. She took a seat by the window, feeling oddly shy and tongue-tied, for after all she and
Nico were still almost strangers to one another. And
yet there had been that indescribable bond of which
she had been aware, sure that he felt it too. And now as
he looked at her across the room she wished she could
confide in him at this moment instead of waiting. Yes,
somewhere at the back of her mind she knew she would
one day confide in him.

And if that were the case, then why not now?

There had to be an opening, and this would never
come while this awkwardness existed between them.

It was Nico who eased the moment by asking how she
and Leon had come to meet.

'I'd have asked him the other evening,' he added,
'but knowing him, I was cagey. Leon has never cared
for being questioned. not about anything at all.'

'We met when I was a nurse,' she answered, smiling at
him. 'Leon had had an accident, and was occupying a
private ward in my wing.'

'It's incredible that he should have wanted to marry
you after such a short acquaintanceship.'

She laughed and only then did he realise he had not
been very tactful.

'Sorry,' he said with a rueful grimace. 'Unless I think
well before I speak I tend to forget tact.'

'It doesn't matter,' she smiled. And then, 'You came
because you thought I'd be glad of the company?'

'Something of the sort,' he admitted. 'I felt you must
be lonely, here on your own. Perhaps you preferred it,
though, seeing that you didn't want to go with Leon to
Athens?'

'I *was* lonely, Nico—I own to it. I'm glad you came;
it was nice of you to think of me.'

He was pleased by her words and it showed in the
way his eyes lit up.

'There's a mystery, isn't there?' he was emboldened to say after a slight hesitation.

'A mystery?'

'About your marriage to Leon——' He stopped as if uncertain about continuing, but Tara, curious to learn anything she could, said encouragingly,

'Do go on, Nico. I'm interested in what you have to say.'

He looked at her perceptively.

'So I was right; there is a mystery. You see, Tara, Leon and Elene have been close friends for the past year and everyone had begun to take their marriage for granted. Then suddenly he went to England on business and came back with you. It's a nine days' wonder among all the people who know him, not only friends but business acquaintances and employees. Elene was very controlled that evening when we came here, but she was very upset when Leon phoned to tell her he was married.'

Tara stared at him for a long moment, going over in her mind what he had said.

'Did they quarrel?' she asked eventually.

'I believe they had a tiff. Elene's very beautiful and the men run after her. She allowed one to take her out——' Nico spread his hands and shrugged. 'It's just a rumour I heard which might or might not be true. I do know that Elene attracted Leon more than any of the other——' He stopped and coloured slightly. 'I've done it again,' he said almost despairingly.

'I know that Leon's had other women,' she said casually. 'It's only to be expected, isn't it?'

'I suppose so. But one doesn't remind a man's wife of such things.'

'Forget it,' she advised. 'Tell me some more about Elene.'

'Well, as I said, she was very upset.' He paused and

looked speculatively at her. 'You really want to know more?' he asked doubtfully.

'Yes, I do, Nico.'

'She believes that Leon married you on the rebound.'

'I see. . . . So she obviously believes he was in love with her?'

He nodded.

'We all believed he was in love with her.'

'Leon is not the man to fall in love,' Tara stated, and, watching for Nico's reaction, she saw his brows shoot up, but then he immediately nodded, not in agreement, but as if he had made a discovery.

'So he isn't in love with you?'

'Neither of us is in love.' It was out, and she knew full well that some explanation would be called for. She was still vague about enlisting his help but was sure that she would attempt to get assistance from him.

'How did he come to ask you to marry him?'

Tara hesitated, feeling that to tell him everything might be risky since she had no idea just how deep the friendship was between him and Leon. She thought of what the consequences might be should Nico, after listening to her story, then go to Leon and repeat it all, out of a sense of loyalty. She had no wish to suffer again from her husband's fury, for the fear he could put into her was very real. Nico was looking at her; he said she had gone pale and asked if she was all right.

She nodded, still hesitant, still afraid. At last she said,

'How deep is your friendship with Leon, Nico?'

'We're not really friends. We live here, on this small island, so it was natural we should get to know one another, and that we'd mix socially. But apart from that we have little in common. Elene has a luxurious house here but spends most of her time in Athens, modelling clothes for the famous fashion house of which Leon is the head.' He paused, examining her face for a moment.

'You can trust me, Tara,' he assured her eventually. 'I feel that you need to confide in someone, but it's natural that you are hesitating. Did you not sense a sort of—— How can I describe it?' he said, considering. 'A bond if you like?'

'That's exactly how I felt, Nico! I'm glad you felt that way too.'

'So we're friends?'

'Yes, we're friends.'

'Then you can answer my question without any fear of my ever repeating anything I hear.'

'Leon did not ask me to marry him,' she said slowly, Nico's surprise bringing a thin smile to her face.

'He didn't ask you?'

'Nico, you're not going to believe the story I'm about to tell you.'

'I don't think you would lie,' he returned emphatically. 'In any case, to do so wouldn't serve any purpose, would it?'

'No,' she agreed. 'But to tell you the truth might just serve a purpose.' She stopped, but he said nothing, and Tara also remained silent because she had no idea how to begin such a fantastic story. However, her uncertainty soon passed and she began at the beginning, and carrying on through the little exclamations that periodically issued from her companion's lips.

'He actually kidnapped you!' gasped Nico when at last she had ended her story. 'Good lord—no one would ever believe such a thing of him! He's a well-known distinguished figure in the capital, respected—— I can't believe it, Tara!'

'You just said you didn't think I would lie,' she reminded him.

'I know. . . .' He seemed dazed still, and his brow was knitted in a frown, as if he were endeavouring mentally to accept what he had heard.

'On your wedding day,' he murmured slowly. 'What

a dreadful thing to do! You must have been heartbroken?'

'Of course I was, and very frightened.'

'But now ...? You seem to have got over it?'

'So much has happened that I seem to be living all
the time in the present, and the past is vague. David is
often real but just as often forgotten completely.'
Mainly when her husband was making love to her, she
thought, but naturally·kept that to herself.

'So you're a prisoner here?' Automatically he glanced
through the window. Davos was over by the fountain,
clearing some weeds from the pond.

'Yes, I'm a prisoner. Leon wants me to promise not to
try to escape and if I do promise he'll take the guards
away.'

'It's diabolical! What the devil got into him! Was he
so mad with Elene that he married the first woman he
set eyes on?'

'I couldn't have been the first woman he set eyes on,
could I? He'd travelled from·Greece to England.'

'He was over there on business and I believe Elene
should have gone with him; she often did. But what
possessed him to commit a criminal act like that? If he
merely wanted you he could——' Nico stopped, looking embarrassed, and Tara eased the moment by asking
if she could give him some refreshments. He said he
would have *ouzo*, and this was brought on a tray after
Tara had rung for a maid. A *mezé c*ame with it, as it
always did. Tara had fresh orange juice. She was not
hungry, she said when Nico offered to share the *mezé*
with her.

'I wonder why he went to·the lengths of marriage,'
Nico decided to say presently. 'He could——' He stopped again and shrugged.

'Have had what he wanted without?' Tara shook her
head. 'As he explained, he'd have been· in serious
trouble with the law, because once he had—er—cast me

off I'd naturally have gone to the police.'

'You can still do that.'

'Only if I escape—and he won't give me any freedom at all until I promise not to escape.'

'But you'd not keep the promise,' he said in astonishment. 'Make it, and then get away.'

'I couldn't go back on my word, Nico.'

'Then you must be crazy! You couldn't possibly consider yourself bound by a promise like that!'

'I could, and Leon knows it.'

He looked at her, his eyes wide with admiration. A flush rose to highlight the beautiful contours of her face and she noticed a sudden movement in his throat, the slow pulsation of a nerve.

'You're a very wonderful person,' he said softly. 'I wish....'

'Yes?' she prompted, hope high within her.

'I could like you very much, Tara.'

She said in response,

'Will you help me to escape, Nico?'

'You'd go back to your fiancé, I suppose?' His voice was bleak, and very quiet.

'I don't know.' She thought of the possibility that she was having a baby. 'He might not want me, after I'd been married to someone else.' She tried to focus David's face but failed to do so. How very strange that she had reached a state of mind where she was not torn with anguish any more! It seemed disloyal to David not to feel desolate at the idea of what she had lost.

'There'd have to be a divorce, or an annulment, and it would take time.'

'All I want at present is to get away from this island,' she said. 'What I do with my life after that is a matter to be decided later. Will you help me?' she asked again.

He looked at her and she knew a struggle was taking place within him.

'You'd denounce Leon to the police. He'd be ruined.'

But she was shaking her head even before he had stopped speaking.

'I couldn't denounce him to the police, Nico.'

He looked puzzled.

'Don't you want revenge?'

'I did at first, but not now.'

'You've not fallen in love with him?'

'Of course not!'

'Many women have. He has an attraction that's quite exceptional.'

She said nothing, but to herself she admitted the truth of what Nico had said. Leon's attraction *was* exceptional; it had brought her to surrender too many times for her to deny it.

'I promise I won't denounce him, Nico . . . please help me.'

'I feel I ought to, Tara, but Leon will find out it was me.'

'How can he?'

'You've thought of some way that I can help you without his knowing?'

'No, unfortunately I haven't. But surely we can think of something?' She was a trifle breathless, with excitement. She had known, somehow, that Nico would help her, known because of that bond that had come between them only a few days ago, at the dinner-party.

'It's not going to be easy.'

The shadow of a bird flashed across the sunlight on the floor and he looked towards the window. Tara, following the direction of his gaze, saw not only Davos, but one of the gardeners as well. Of course, it was only to be expected that the gardener would be working out there, but she had become so conscious of being watched that she resented even the sight of any of her husband's servants.

'I agree it's not going to be easy,' she said, 'but, Nico, I shall go mad if I don't get away soon.'

He stirred uneasily in his seat.

'What a mess! The man must have been out of his mind to do a thing like that! It's so uncharacteristic of him; he's level-headed, law-abiding—usually,' he added as he saw the lift of Tara's brows. 'How long is he going to be in Athens?'

'Until Saturday, so he told me.'

'Three days more....' Again Nico's eyes wandered to the window. 'How the devil are we to get rid of these fellows?'

'I don't know. Davos probably sleeps in the corridor all night, so he can be on hand if I try to leave my bedroom.'

'My God! I'm beginning to feel sure that Leon's mad!'

Tara knew that was not so, knew that the reason for any action of Leon's that concerned her was the result of his all-consuming desire for her.

'I could probably get out of the window,' she suggested thoughtfully. 'If you could come when everyone's in bed and put a ladder outside for me. There are several ladders in a shed at the bottom of the orchard——' She looked at him anxiously. 'Could you do that, Nico?'

'I suppose so.'

'You seem doubtful.'

'It isn't that,' he said rather flatly. 'It's just the idea that, once away from here, you'll never see me again.'

She bit her lip.

'I'm asking you to help me and yet not giving anything in return.' Her eyes were shadowed as she added, 'It isn't fair of me, is it? You'd have to take me to Piraeus on your boat—— No, it isn't fair for me to expect all that from you without offering anything in return.'

'You said you weren't sure you would go back to your fiancé.'

'I know what you're thinking, Nico, but I must be honest, I could never feel anything for you—not anything deep.'

'You can't say a thing like that. We haven't had a chance of getting to know one another. Yet even so there's already this bond we have both felt. Surely that's a basis for something stronger?'

She gave a small sigh. It would seem that Nico had an affection for her, which seemed absurd in the face of the fact that the Greek male was notorious for his lack of deep feeling.

'I really don't think I could fall in love with you, Nico,' she said. 'Besides, if I got away from here I should naturally go back to my own country.'

He nodded his head.

'That is what I was saying a moment ago. You'd never see me again.' He lifted his glass and stared at the cloudy liquid contained in it, then put it to his lips, regarding Tara over its narrow rim. 'I'll help you all the same,' he promised. 'But it can't be during this particular absence of Leon's because my boat is having some repairs done to it. When will Leon be going away again?'

'I don't know.' Her heart had been throbbing with hope and excitement and now it felt like lead within her. 'Is there no possible way I can leave within the next couple of days, Nico? I mean—is there not another boat I could get?'

'I've a friend who has a motor launch, but I would not care to trust him to keep quiet—or even to take you in fact, because he's a business associate of Leon's. He's in the wine business and I understand he buys grapes from Leon.'

'Leon has vineyards?' said Tara, for the moment diverted.

'Yes, on the mainland. Leon has many business interests besides fashion. In fact, fashion's only a small part of his overall activities. I suppose you know he's a millionaire?'

'I knew he must be wealthy,' returned Tara without much interest. She was back to the matter of her escape, feeling that she had been raised in spirit only to find herself right back to where she was. Nico, sensing her disappointment, apologised and said he would make sure that everything was ready for the next occasion when Leon was absent, and with that Tara had to be satisfied. Before he left Nico asked if he could call again, and although Tara felt it was risky, and told him so, he was willing to take the risk.

'If any of these damned servants thinks fit to carry tales to Leon then let them!' he said.

'But, when I've escaped, Leon will immediately suspect you of helping me.'

'I don't really care. If he cuts up rough I shall tell him he had better watch his step because of what I know.'

After he had left Tara was frowning over what he had said. She did not care for the idea that Leon should be subjected to the kind of embarrassment which Nico could, if he so wished, inflict upon him.

And yet why should she care about her husband's feelings? He certainly had not cared about hers when he callously parted her from her fiancé on their wedding day, nor since, when he had forced his will upon her.

# CHAPTER TEN

From high on the hillside came the tinkle of goat bells, then from lower down the hoarse bray of a donkey as it brought its rider up the cobblestoned path towards a steep flight of steps that had been painted white by the owners of the house to which they led. Tara, standing on the edge of a copse at the southern end of the garden, watched broodingly for her husband's tall figure, as she had seen the ferry boat come in and knew he would be on it. There he was, a suitcase in his hand, coming along from the harbour towards the path which wound its way in a series of steep and sinuous bends off which were cut the paths to the various great mansions which were part of the attraction of the tiny island of Hydra.

Seeing her standing there, Leon lifted a hand; she waved in response, one part of her shrinking from what she knew she must expect, while, paradoxically, the other part actually hungered for the thrill of her husband's demands. She wished she could understand herself, and her attitude towards the man who had her at his mercy. She told herself that she hated him; her one obsession was to get away from him ... and yet.... He had hinted that she would miss his passionate lovemaking and she had since dwelt on those confident words, aware as she was of her husband's fascination for her, the magnetism which drew her irresistibly, compelling her to obey his arrogant orders, to surrender to the mastery of his ardent demands. Was sex all she thought about? she had asked herself with contempt. Did the fire of his passion consume her totally, filling her heart and mind—and even her soul—to the exclusion of all else. What but disaster could be the outcome of this kind of imprisonment? She was an idealist who put loving and caring before all else . . . or she had done so until she met this Greek pagan who had set out to teach her about very different emotions.

'How nice to have my wife waiting for me,' he commented with mocking amusement as he came up to her at last. 'Missed me, obviously.'

She glared at him, teeth gritting. Why did he have to rile her like this?

'It was nothing more than sheer boredom that brought me out here,' she snapped, turning abruptly away in the direction of the house.

He fell into step beside her and took her hand.

'What have you been doing with yourself?' he asked casually, ignoring her peevishly-spoken complaint.

'Reading and sunbathing—then more reading and sunbathing,' she answered sarcastically. 'I had meals in between, and sometimes I was diverted by watching my jailers and wondering what they would do were I to make a run for it.'

'They can run swifter than you,' he said.

'I don't know. . . . I believe I'd give them a few breathless moments.'

'And you, my child,' he returned cheerfully, 'will be having a few painful moments if you don't change your mood. I've been expecting an eager welcome, but instead I've a little vixen awaiting me with snapping teeth.'

She fell silent, trying to divert her mind to more pleasant things—the Judas and arbutus trees gilded by sunshine, the oleanders by the fountain's edge, the poinsettias and the lavender hedge, with butterflies gleaming iridescent as they hovered above the flowers, like huming-birds. The goatherd on the hillside, the cliff paths down to the sleepy harbour where fishermen sat mending their nets or slapping octopus to a frothy lather on the stones. In the olive trees cicadas trilled, their music slightly distorted by the sough of the wind in the foliage. She wandered along at her husband's side, glad that he was silent. She would hear his voice soon enough!

'Come up and unpack for me,' commanded Leon as soon as they entered the house. 'You can tell me what you have really been doing.'

She obeyed, saying as they mounted the wide, balus-traded staircase,

'I've told you what I've been doing.'

'Nothing else?' He stood for a moment, his hand on the door knob, his eyes regarding her intently. 'You should have given me that promise, you know. You'll have to give it in the end.'

She lowered her lashes, avoiding that close scrutiny, for she was thinking about Nico and his promise to get her away from here the next time Leon was absent from home.

In the bedroom Leon put down the suitcase and held out his hands.

'Come to me,' he ordered in a soft tone of voice.

Anger surged, but she obeyed, accepting the fact that there was no escape anyway, so it was far less painful to go to him willingly than to have him leap across the room to grip her wrist in a bruising hold. 'Kiss me.' Again she obeyed, giving him a tight-lipped peck. She was caught roughly to him, caught in a brutal embrace that made her gasp with sudden pain. 'I'll teach you yet, my girl! I thought you had come to realise that I'm your master!'

'I hate you,' she gasped, 'hate you, do you hear!'

'I daresay all the household can hear,' he responded darkly. 'As to your assertion that you hate me—repeti-tion makes it less convincing. You know in your heart of hearts that you don't hate me, Tara.' So confident he was! What a lesson he would learn if she did make her escape! She looked at his face above her, dark and satanic, the eyes burning with desire. A hand came up to trace the curve of her shoulder from her throat and then to the lobe of her ear. 'You might hate the idea of obeying me, of accepting my word as law, but you don't hate *me*. On the contrary, I firmly believe that you've reached the stage where you're realising that there can be no real hate where the physical pleasures we give each other are so great.'

She looked away, sure that she hated him in spite of the argument he had produced against it.

'It's only desires of the flesh,' she managed to say at length. 'And that's only effective at the time——' She broke off, blushing, but brought her gaze back to his. 'You know what I mean,' she ended, fully expecting a smile of mocking amusement to curve his lips, and not being disappointed.

'Yes, Tara, I know what you mean.'

'As I said, it's effective at the time, but not after-wards.'

'What you're trying to say is that lovemaking impairs judgment, is that it?' She merely nodded and he added with some amusement, 'But it's bound to, isn't it? No one can be clear-headed when in the throes of a violent passion——'

'Oh, be quiet!' She twisted out of his hold and ran to the other side of the room. 'Don't you ever think of any-thing but *that*!'

'I thought we were merely discussing the question of whether one could be capable of rational thought at a time like that.'

She sighed impatiently.

'We were talking about my hatred for you, Leon! I suppose that I don't hate you then—but I do after-wards, all the time.' She looked directly into his eyes. 'Don't fool yourself,' she advised, 'because no matter

how you try to, you'll know in the end that you were
wrong.'

His eyes were suddenly alert.

'What exactly do you mean?' he demanded tautly.
'If you're up to something, Tara, then I recommend
strongly that you remember what I once said to you: I
have never been taken unawares in the whole of my
life.'

Well, there was always a first time, she thought. However, she realised that she had almost made a slip; she
resolved to practise caution all the time from now on.

'I don't know what you're talking about,' she returned with well-feigned innocence. 'What can I be up
to, with all these jailers watching my every move?'

He opened his mouth, then closed it again, much to
her relief. He went to his own room and she did not
see him again until much later in the day.


It was the following morning that Leon asked her again
to make the promise to him.

'You might just as well give it,' he advised with a
hint of asperity. 'Because if you don't I shall keep you
prisoner here until our child is born—which will be an
inconvenience to me as well as to you.'

'It will inconvenience you?' She looked at him questioningly.

'I want to take you to Athens with me the next time
I go. My business associates know I'm married, and
they were puzzled that I went over on my own. I don't
want to do so again because it will look very odd.'

'I can understand that,' she returned.

'But not sympathise,' he said evenly.

'Why should I sympathise with you?'

'Are you going to give me the promise?' he repeated
with growing impatience.

'No, I am not. I can't make a promise which I have
no intention of keeping.' She was troubled lest he

should defer his next visit to the capital indefinitely.
He had once said that it was his usual practice to go
over about once a fortnight and stay for several days,
but from what he had just said it was plain that he was
reluctant to go without his wife. As he had mentioned,
his friends and business associates would consider it
very strange, to leave his new wife alone at home.

'So you're still hoping you will find a way of running
from me?' His eyes were narrowed, and a trifle anxious,
she thought. She had come to breakfast a quarter of an
hour later than he, and he had waited for her, drawing
out her chair and remarking at the same time on her
appearance. She looked charming, he told her with a
smile. She was in a pretty long-sleeved blouse of wild
silk and a pair of sapphire blue slacks. Her hair shone
and even her eyes had lost their sadness. He remarked
on that, too, but she had merely shrugged and made no
comment. But it had naturally crossed her mind that it
must be the hope in her heart that had taken the
shadows from her eyes. If only Leon would keep to his
practice and go off to Athens again in a fortnight's
time. She was sure Nico would manage to get her away
to Piraeus, where she would be free! Free to get
the first plane for England!

She looked at him across the table, strangely affected
by that hint of anxiety in his gaze.

'You know I'm hoping to run from you, Leon,' she
answered quietly. 'You must have realised right from
the start that escape would remain my one burning
ambition.'

'If you went you'd take my child with you.' His voice
was harsh suddenly and a kindling look came to his
eyes.

'If I escape before it's born, yes—— Oh, why are we
discussing the child! I'm *not* having one! You seem so
sure, but you could be wrong—I hope to God you are!'

I've suffered enough at your hands without that being added to my misery!'

A strange pallor seemed to be creeping under the tan of his cheeks, and she noticed a movement there, too, like the twitching of a nerve out of control.

'If you would only accept your lot,' he began, when she interrupted him to say she never would accept it.

'Why should I?' she added with fervour. 'Does any prisoner, taken the way I was taken, accept his lot?'

'You're mine!' he stated firmly, 'and the sooner you admit it the happier you'll be!'

She sighed and said in a flat little tone,

'Can we change the subject, Leon? I'm not up to an argument this morning.'

His eyes glinted but he made no comment and they ate their grapefruit in silence. Stamati came in with a silver tray and served them with eggs and bacon and mushrooms. When he had gone Tara said, hoping she sounded casual,

'When will you be going to Athens again?'

'Why?' he countered briefly, picking up his knife and fork.

'No particular reason,' she shrugged. 'I just wondered, that was all.'

'I shan't be going yet awhile. I want that promise so that I can take you along with me.'

Her heart jerked. Surely he would have to go! He could not leave his various businesses indefinitely.

'You'll have a long time to wait for my promise,' she warned. 'I'm sure your commitments in Athens won't keep that long.'

His shrewd eyes seemed to bore right into her. Fear set her nerves rioting. Oh, God, she whispered, make him go. Let there be an emergency—anything! But *make* him go!

'You sound as if you want me away,' he said smoothly at last. 'Any particular reason?' Soft the tone, and challenging. Tara shook her head and paid no attention to the food on her plate. 'If you think for one moment that my servants will risk losing their jobs by being careless then let me tell you it's wishful thinking on your part. Why don't you be sensible and let me have the promise?'

She gave a shuddering sigh, feeling defeated. But the next moment an idea had come to her and her spirits lifted. She was careful not to reveal this in her manner as she replied, deliberately injecting a note of despair into her voice.

'Perhaps I will in the end be driven to making the promise.' Another shuddering sigh, audible this time, and her shoulders drooped. 'You've won every round so far, haven't you, Leon? So why shouldn't you win this one?' Her lip quivered and she put down her knife and fork as if she no longer had any appetite for the food in front of her.

'So you are beginning to see sense.' The satisfaction in his eyes was apparent, and a smile curved his lips. 'I knew you'd come round in the end.'

She looked at him, swallowing convulsively ... and praying he had noticed. She wanted to ensure he was aware of her reluctance to make the promise, while at the same time giving him the impression that she was resigned to giving it.

'I'm not making it yet,' she told him, but in a quivering, defeated sort of voice. 'My spirit's not yet broken altogether—in spite of your efforts.'

'I've no wish to break your spirit!'

'Oh, yes, you have. How many times have you told me I must regard you as my master? How many times have you coerced me into doing what you want me to?'

'All I want is for you to stop fighting me.'

She shrugged, unwilling to continue the discussion. And it was Leon who broke the silence, a few minutes later after Stamati had been in to clear away the dishes they had been using.

'If you're resigned to giving the promise you might as well give it now. You've seen nothing of this island—nothing beyond the grounds of this house. You're a very foolish child, Tara.'

'I can't give the promise yet. I must think about it—please give me time,' she added in a pleading voice, feeling a hypocrite and blaming her husband for driving her to such spurious lengths. She had always been open and honest, but now, for the first time in her life, she was deliberately practising deceit.

'Yes, I'll give you time,' agreed Leon, but with an exasperated intake of his breath. 'I suppose I haven't any option.'

His glance revealed his thoughts; he was thinking she was just about as stubborn as it was possible to be. Well, let him think what he liked, so long as he didn't guess what she was about.

And it was evident that he had not guessed when, about ten days later, he announced his intention of going to Athens.

'I'd like to take you,' he said, glancing at her with a hopeful expression. 'How about that promise, Tara?'

She shook her head.

'Perhaps I shall come with you the next time.' She had to lower her head, ashamed of her deceit. 'Have a nice trip, Leon.'

'It's purely business. Had you been coming with me it would have been different. I'd have taken you around. You'll like Athens, Tara; there's so much to do and see.'

'I have heard that it's interesting, and thought I'd like to see it one day.'

'Then come with me?' His voice was low and persuasive, and not in any way commanding or arrogant. Her eyes flew to his; to her amazement she was thinking that it would be rather nice to be going with him. And if she gave the promise she could go with him.

But she would then have burned her boats for ever. Once the promise was given her sense of honour would never allow her to go back on her word.

'Next time,' she said again, and with that he had to be satisfied.

She was in the bedroom when he was ready to leave and he came to her, took her in his arms and kissed her on the lips.

'You have so much to offer me,' he told her, his black eyes looking deeply into hers. 'Your body when it moves against me is wonderful! Move again,' he said gruffly. 'And again.' She did as she was told and within seconds his passion had flared. But he had to let her go, as the ferry was leaving in half an hour's time. Tara stood on the terrace and watching him make his way down to the harbour, buoyancy and youth in every step he took. She caught her breath, thinking of his attractiveness and the easy way he could use his power and his magnetism to draw her to him. He had stated emphatically that she would miss his lovemaking if she left him, and she had secretly admitted that it was true.

He was lost to sight at last and she turned back to the house. Nico would come; she was sure of it. The last time Leon was away Nico had visited her three times, and she had been half afraid that one of her husband's servants might just mention the fact to his master. But, aware of the wide gap between master and servant in Greece, and especially in Leon's household, she had not been too anxious. She wandered about the grounds during the afternoon, restless and expectant, waiting for Nico to come. Perhaps, she thought as the hours dragged by, Nico was not aware of Leon's absence from home—or perhaps he had changed his mind about helping her, considering it was not worth the trouble, seeing that he was gaining absolutely nothing from it.

Dinner time arrived and he still had not come, but just as Tara was about to sit down Stamati came to the dining-room to tell her that a visitor had arrived.

'Miss Flourou, madam. She asked for Mr Leon, but I told her he was away. She's in the sitting-room, madam.'

Elene! She had come to see Leon. . . .

'See that my dinner's kept hot, please, Stamati,' she said, and went along to the sitting-room where Elene was seated on the sofa, a cigarette in her long, perfectly-manicured fingers.

'Good evening,' Tara greeted her, marvelling at the cool and dignified manner she was able to adopt. 'You wanted to see Leon——'

'He's away, so Stamati said. I had need to discuss something with him about the coming fashion show in Athens. I'm sorry I missed him. He went today?'

'Yes.'

'I'll see him when he comes back.' The girl cast her a scornful glance and immediately Tara was conscious of her clothes. Dining alone, she had not troubled to change out of the slacks and shirt she had been wearing during the afternoon. 'Did you not want to go with him?' asked Elene curiously.

'No; I like it here.'

'But, since you're newly married, I should have thought you'd want to be with him.'

'I shall probably go with him the next time.' Tara sat down, feeling uncomfortable and wishing the girl would leave. There seemed no reason why she should have stayed in the first place, seeing that the man she had come to see was away.

'He'll be very busy the next time. We have a most important fashion show on, with buyers coming from Britain and Paris and America.' She spoke condescendingly, as if determined to impress Tara with the knowledge that she knew everything about the House of Hera, while Tara knew nothing. 'I suppose,' added

Elene slowly, 'you know that I am Leon's top model?'

'He did mention something about it,' replied Tara in a casual tone.

Elene's eyes glinted.

'Without me, Leon would be lost.'

'He would?' with a slight lift of Tara's brows. 'But surely no one is indispensable?'

Colour flooded Elene's cheeks. She drew on her cigarette and exhaled, her narrowed gaze fixed on Tara through a film of smoke.

'Did you know that Leon was practically engaged to me?'

Tara gave a start.

'That's a strange thing to say to his wife, isn't it?'

Elene shrugged. Looking at her intently, Tara saw that she was very close to tears.

'He let me down badly. Everyone else knows about it, so I don't see why you shouldn't.' Elene inhaled deeply, her dark eyes fixed and brooding. Tara had the impression that the girl was talking like this because she had to—she could not help herself. And from this impression another was born: Elene was boiling over inside, crazed with jealousy of Leon's wife. 'I don't know how you and he met, or how you came to get married, but I do know that he married you from a feeling of pique, because he and I had quarrelled—oh, it wasn't anything really serious, even. He was angry because he thought I'd——' She stopped, frowning, angry with herself, apparently, for revealing so much. And yet within the space of less than ten seconds she was saying, 'Leon's like that, unpredictable, impulsive.'

Tara was shaking her head.

'My husband would never be impulsive,' she argued. 'Why do you say such a thing?'

'Because of the speed with which he married you.' Elene crushed the cigarette out in an ashtray and proceeded to extract another from the gold case that lay on the table. 'He couldn't have known you any time at all?' A question which Tara chose to ignore. 'How long did he know you?' persisted Elene, flicking a lighter and setting it to the tip of the cigarette.

'I don't think it matters to anyone how long he knew me.'

'He's not in love with you—— No, don't interrupt! If he was in love with you then he'd have wanted you with him. He's been away twice now and you haven't gone with him.' She looked directly at her. 'He would never ever have gone away without me—when we were keeping company, that is.'

'I could have gone with him,' said Tara. 'But I chose to stay at home.'

'Then obviously you don't love him either. Did you marry him for his money?'

Tara gasped incredulously. The girl was so mad with jealousy and anger that she seemed not to care what she said. Rising from her chair, Tara said quietly, and with a wave of the hand in the direction of the door,

'As it was Leon you came to see I'm sure you will not be wanting to stay. My dinner will be spoiling. I'll tell my husband that you called, and he'll probably be in touch by telephone.'

She heard Elene's teeth snap together, but she rose at once and moved gracefully to the door.

'Goodnight,' she almost spat out, her dark eyes again roving Tara's figure contemptuously.

'Goodnight, Miss Flourou.'

Tara went to the front door with her—although it was Stamati who was there to open it and close it after her.

'Your dinner will be served at once, Mrs Leon.'

'Thank you, Stamati.' She looked at the man, noticing his expression and recalling Kleanthes' amazement when Leon introduced her as his wife.

'Your wife, *Kirie* Leon!' Kleanthes had exclaimed.

'But what about Miss——?' He had obviously been going to mention Elene's name but had managed to stop himself in time. All Leon's servants—and indeed almost everyone on this small island—must have known of the close relationship which had existed between Leon and his model. And everyone seemed to have expected him to marry her.

Did he care for her? Tara could not imagine his caring for anyone but himself. Love was something about which he knew nothing.

# CHAPTER ELEVEN

THE waiting for Nico seemed interminable. Tara had risen early, which made the day longer and more trying to the nerves. Leon had been non-committal about how long he would be away, so Tara had not the faintest idea when to expect him back. He could be back tomorrow, or even tonight—— No, not tonight. He could not possibly get through all his business in less than two days.

'Oh, Nico—why don't you come!'

She went from room to room in the house, admiring the large, marble-paved rooms with their finely-carved ceilings, and cornices, their lovely antique furniture, their exquisite porcelain-filled cabinets, trying all the while to fix her attention on things other than the idea of getting away from here. Through one huge window she saw the marble fountain and was drawn into the grounds. Here was peace, usually, but today everything in her was unrest, anxiety and uncertainty. She knew that if Nico should let her down she would feel that her life was finished, for she would have to give Leon the promise or go raving mad! She could not stand this imprisonment much longer. Also, if she should be pregnant, and the child was born here, then she would indeed be unable to gain her freedom—at least, not for years and years, because after one child there would be another, and perhaps another.

She wandered listlessly about the garden, glancing at her watch about every ten minutes or so. 'Nico,' she whispered fervently, 'please come.'

She was working herself up into a state of near hysteria and decided to do something about it. She went inside for a book but, back in the garden, she found she could not concentrate. Even the flowers with their exotic perfumes made no impression on her, nor the gossamer-winged butterflies skimming through a patch of starry white blossoms to settle on the passion flowers. All of these things had fascinated her up till now, but as she walked, the book in her hand, she saw nothing except the wide expanse of sea beyond the busy harbour ... the sea over which she had expected to travel to freedom.

Davos and Kleanthes were in the orchard, spraying the orange and lemon trees; she saw Davos glance up because of something said by his companion and when Tara followed the direction of his eyes she saw a man coming up the steep path leading to the gate. Both men stopped and waited, but Tara turned away, concluding the the man had come to see one of the servants. She was on the patio, the book open on her lap, when Kleanthes brought the man to her.

'I haf a letter for Mrs Leon,' the man said, but did not offer it to her. 'It was forgotten when the post was brought up this morning. It might be important, so I bring it for you.' The man spoke with a pronounced accent, and he pushed a hand through his hair and gave a little gasp as he added, 'It is so hot! I very thirsty for big glass of water!' His gaze was fixed—wooden almost—as he stared into Tara's eyes. With lightning speed she grasped everything and, turning to Kleanthes, she said,

'Bring a glass of water—— Or perhaps you would like a fruit drink?' she amended, looking at the man.

'Very nice! Plenty much orange juice!'

Kleanthes inclined his head, but, about to move away, he said curiously,

'I haven't seen you before.'

'I haf come to visit my sister; she is the post—post—lady?' it was a question, because obviously he did not include 'post mistress' in his vocabulary.

'She has many brothers,' said Kleanthes with a careless shrug. 'Welcome to our island!'

'*Efkharisto poli!*' returned the man with a huge smile
which revealed several bright gold fillings.

'I bring the drink for you,' said Kleanthes, and
walked away. The man sat down at Tara's invitation
and withdrew an envelope from his pocket. She held it
for a moment, as a fit of trembling seized her. What did
the note contain ... good news or bad? Either Nico was
going to assist her as promised, or he had sent an
apology for not being able to do so.

Her fingers moved over the envelope and she realised
that there was a pencil inside it. So Nico wanted an
answer! With hopes soaring she swiftly slit the top of
the envelope and withdrew the folded sheet of paper.

'I am Savvas,' said the man. 'I take answer to Mr
Nico.'

Tara nodded absently; she was already reading.

'Before you read further, write on the envelope the
exact location of your bedroom and give it to Savvas.'

This was written in bold capitals at the top of the
single sheet of paper. Tara immediately did as in-
structed, passing the envelope back to Savvas. Her heart
was pounding against her chest. She felt that already
she was free.

The man put the envelope into his pocket and sat
back. Kleanthes returned, having been gone less than
two minutes. Tara could see the reason for those urgent
instructions; there might or might not be much time
during which Tara was alone with Savvas, Nico had
thought, and in consequence had even provided the
pencil.

Kleanthes stood and watched Savvas drink thirstily,
then accompanied him back to the gate. Tara had
slipped the letter into her pocket and she rose, casually,
and entered the house. In her bedroom, she began to

read the letter, her heart still beating overrate.

'Dear Tara,' it began, 'Although I knew, yesterday, that Leon had caught the early ferry, I felt it best not to come up—and I know that you must feel the same. It is best to maintain total secrecy if possible. So I sailed to Poros yesterday and picked up a man who has often done casual work for me on the boat. No one on Hydra knows Savvas, so the little ruse I worked out will succeed. The plan is this: I want you to be ready at two o'clock tomorrow morning, when I shall be putting the ladder up to your window. I expect you will want to bring clothes. Wrap them into a bundle and drop them out of the window. I shall provide the suitcase to put them in. The bundle will make no sound, whereas a suitcase might waken someone in the house. Also, have a folded blanket on the sill, so that the ladder will rest on it silently. That is all you have to do. I am sending Savvas back to Poros on the seven o'clock ferry this evening, so he will be well out of the way. My boat is ready and will take you to Piraeus. I don't know why I do this. Perhaps it is exciting, or perhaps I like to rescue a maiden in distress. Or it might be that I like you very much.' It was signed with his name, nothing more. Tara tore the paper into tiny pieces, and flushed them away in the toilet.

Never had Tara known time to drag as it did between the reading of Nico's letter and the moment when, silently opening the window, she laid the folded blanket on the sill. All was ready and she peered down into the inky darkness of the garden, her heart throbbing wildly, every nerve tensed. No sound or sign of movement. Her bundle of clothes was on the sill, ready to be thrown down as soon as the ladder came up. Yes! The shadowy impression of a human form ... the ladder was raised and she held her breath, terrified that it would sway with its own weight and crash into one

of the other windows. But Nico was strong and the
ladder came into place. Tara dropped the bundle, and
was just about to step through the window on to the
ladder when she saw the shadowy figure move, then
race away to the black outline of a copse at the end of
the lawn. Petrified, she saw another shadowy figure,
tall, with a springing step. . . .

Her heart seemed for a moment to stop beating altogether. It wasn't true! Leon could not possibly be
here at this time of the night! But who else had that
tall lithe frame? Sheer terror kept her rooted to the
spot as she watched the figure stand and stare, then
stoop to pick up the bundle. The next instant the
bundle was flung down again and she sensed rather
than saw the savage kick it received; the oath that accompanied it she heard plainly, and she felt almost
faint with fear.

She was still rooted to the spot when her husband
walked into the bedroom, his face twisted into lines so
evil that he seemed to her terrified imagination to be
Hades himself. What would he do to her? She had seen
him in the grip of fury many times, but never had she
seen him like this. He would murder her, she thought,
a terrified hand going to her throat. Yes, he would
strangle her——

'Who was helping you?' The very quietness of the
voice shot suffocating fear through her whole body; she
felt physically sick and could not speak a word even if
she had wanted to. 'I asked you a question!' The pagan
voice was a whiplash now, but still quiet. She swallowed convulsively, tears starting to her eyes.

'I w-won't—won't t-tell—you——'

'By God, you will—if I have to get it out of you by
torture!' His leap was silent, the grip on her trembling
hand a vice that made her cry out with the excruciating
pain of it. 'Answer me!' he snarled, the thin lips curled
back so that the teeth were bared . . . like those of a tiger

ready for the kill! 'Answer me before I choke the life out of you!'

'I c-can't.' She lifted her face and she knew it was drained of every vestige of colour. She wondered how he had had the luck to arrive home at the exact time she was to have escaped from his ruthless clutches. He had the devil's own luck always—he *was* the devil! 'Please d-don't ask me to—to do what I can't in honour——'

'Honour!' he cut in violently. 'You speak to me of honour?' The black eyes raked her trembling body with the sort of contempt that made her cringe. Sheer rage caused him to pause before being able to continue. 'That pose you adopted for my benefit—the stratagem of acting as if you were defeated and would have to make the promise. The way you gave me the impression that you were resigned—you even said that as I had won every round I was bound to win this! And all the time you were putting me off, playing for time because this attempt at escape had already been planned, hadn't it—hadn't it!' He jerked her body forward and thrust her head right back with his hand beneath her chin. His hand remained there and she was compelled to look at him, look into the fiery rage of those fierce black eyes. 'Hadn't it?' he repeated again.

She nodded, wondering if she would collapse in a heap when he released her.

'Yes, it w-was.'

'With whom? It must be one of the servants that you bribed, because there isn't anyone else who could possibly have helped you!'

'It wasn't one of the servants——'

'Don't lie——' His passion overcame him and he shook her unmercifully. 'I've had enough of your deceit——'

'I had every right to deceive you!' How she managed to conjure up the strength and courage to say that she would never know. But for her trouble she was shaken again, and then that hand came to her throat and she felt the threat of long lean fingers curled menacingly around it. The pressure sent the blood pounding in her head; she struggled in the steel hawser of his hold, twisting about, fighting for her very life. 'Tell me,' he said in a very soft tone when he had withdrawn his hand. 'Tell me who you were making your plans with while you were putting me off by your sly, cunning evasion?'

She did not know why the words 'sly' and 'cunning' should have inflamed her, but they did. With a swift movement that took him unawares she was out of his hold and on the other side of the room, close to the open window.

'I had every right to make plans!' she flashed at him defiantly. 'Every prisoner has the right to attempt escape. How dare you accuse me of being underhand when I was only trying to help myself?' These were mild words in comparison to what he had used, but they seemed to add to his rage.

'I'm still waiting to hear the name of your accomplice!' he snarled, taking a step towards her. 'Who is he?'

She was right against the window, conscious of the breeze against her back. To jump.... Surely injury that way was preferable to the injury her husband was ready to inflict upon her. She felt the sill with clammy hands behind her back, and gripped it, yet did not know how she was going to get on to it before her husband, guessing at her intent, bounded across the room and dragged her back. He would spare her no punishment for an act like that, she thought, and almost abandoned the idea. But that dark and evil countenance, those terrifying eyes, that snarling mouth—and above all those hands of unbelievable strength.... All these influenced her mind and with a twist of her body and a spring upwards she was sitting on the sill.

'I'll jump!' she cried, a ring of triumph in her voice. 'Get ready——'

'Stop! You damned fool—stop!' He was afraid! For the first time in his life probably—he was actually afraid! He moved and her cry halted him on the instant.

'Take another step and I'll fling myself out of this window!'

'Tara—don't be such a fool!' His voice had lost some of its ferocity but by no means all, and she knew for sure that if he could get her inside the room again her situation would be no different from before. Her refusal to inform against Nico had acted as fuel to the already white-hot conflagration of his wrath, and if she should overcome the advantage she had gained he would show her no mercy. 'Come down from there!' he ordered. 'Do as I say, this minute!'

'This is no time for giving me orders,' she flashed, a trifle bewildered that she had been able to win a round at last. 'For a change, I happen to have the whip hand. I shall injure myself rather than have *you* injure me, Leon.'

She heard his teeth grit together, saw his hands clench at his sides in a sort of frustrated gesture. Exultation swept over her, vanquishing most of her fear, because she knew without doubt that he would not let her jump. And so he would have to capitulate. What a blow that would be to his innate Greek egotism!

He stood, irresolute, blind with rage at the knowledge of his defeat.

'Come down,' he said, and this time his voice was almost persuasive.

'Not until you've promised not to use violence on me to make me tell you who put this ladder up here——' She turned to indicate the ladder, and then a scream left her lips as, losing her balance on the precarious perch she was occupying, she felt herself about to fall.

With incredible speed Leon cleared the intervening space and, grabbing at her clothing, he managed to drag her back into the room. She fell against him, sobbing bitterly as she clung to the lapels of his coat. He held her, but she found no gentleness in his arms, nor did he speak any soothing words to her. His body was hard and taut; when eventually she became more composed, and looked up at him, her heart failed her, for his wrath was as fearsome as ever.

'You damned little fool!' he thundered when at last she had managed to suppress her sobs. 'I ought to take a horsewhip to you for behaving like that!' But instead he jerked her body close to his, forced her face up and, bending his head, he crushed her trembling lips with his hard and ruthless mouth. She tried to get away, but by now she had little strength left. In fact, she was utterly drained and weary. But her husband had neither sympathy nor mercy for her condition. She had pierced his pride by offering him an ultimatum which he could not ignore. Another moment and he would have humbled himself sufficiently to have made her the promise she demanded. He gazed down with merciless indifference to her distress, and took her lips beneath his again and again, punishing her for what she had done.

At last he put her from him and closed the window. She watched his tall figure as he turned again. He had saved her life ... but for what? His own pleasure, that was all. His eyes were darkly murderous as he met her misty gaze, his thin mouth more cruel than she had ever seen it. With a little moan she saw him coming closer, felt the steely pressure of his long brown fingers as he gripped her arms and brought her to him.

'I shall question you again in the morning,' he warned. 'But for now——' He kissed her and she quivered in his arms. She had asked for it, she told herself one moment, while the next she was reminded of the fact that she was here only because of his compulsion. 'I did warn you,' he said after a long while, 'that I am never taken unawares, didn't I?'

She nodded and said meekly,

'Yes, Leon, you did.'

'Do you know why I came to be here tonight?'

'No,' she returned, her breath shortening on a little sob.

'But you would like to know, wouldn't you?'

She shook her head wearily.

'You always win,' she quivered, 'and you always will.'

'You've given up hope of running away from me?'

She swallowed thickly, her heart weeping in the full knowledge that only a miracle could save her now.

'Yes ... I think so,' she answered in response to the little shake he gave her as a reminder that she had not answered at once.

'It was this afternoon that I began going over what you'd said about making me the promise later. You said you would have to have time to think about it. Well, the whole thing seemed suddenly to become phoney. I caught on to the idea that you weren't sincere and from that your whole manner stood out as a ruse to deceive me, to dupe me—and I like a fool had swallowed the bait!' For one terrified moment Tara thought he would punish her again. 'I couldn't understand how I had come to accept it all, and then I realised it was because I trusted you! Well, I trusted you no longer. I hired a racing launch in Piraeus and came here as fast as the engine would carry me....' He paused and to her surprise she saw his mouth quiver, and there were little beads of perspiration glistening on his forehead. 'What I have I hold, wife, and perhaps now you will accept me as your husband—and your master?'

She sighed and turned her head from him. He

brought it back, his eyes dark and fierce as they compelled hers to meet them.

'Tomorrow,' she faltered, 'are you going to ill-treat me again?'

'Ill-treat?' His hand was unbuttoning the front of her blouse as he spoke.

'To try and make me tell you who put the ladder there?'

'I shall question you, yes, but I shall also question the servants. There isn't one of them who would dare to lie to me.'

Tara thought of the letter and knew that either Davos or Kleanthes would tell Leon about it. A shuddering sigh that was almost a sob shook her body. Tomorrow would be another ordeal for her.

'I shall never tell you,' she whispered hoarsely. 'You can kill me, but I'll never let you know who helped me.'

'I shan't kill you....' The blouse dropped from his hand and his lips began to explore the tender curve above the lacy bra she wore. Slowly, as if he enjoyed every second, he removed the bra. 'I enjoy you far too much, wife! Never have I derived greater pleasure from a woman than I have from you.' His wandering mouth found her breast, while the other was crushed in his lean fingers. Despite her tiredness she was alive to his powerful magnetism and a thrill of anticipation was already spreading throughout her body. She quivered as, unzipping her skirt, he brought his hand against her flesh as he brought it down. 'Step out of it,' he commanded, and held her away so that she could obey him. Delicate, transient colour stained her cheeks and he laughed. 'You can still blush, child. It is rather touching—certainly it's delectable.' He drew her to him again, putting the toe of an elegant suede shoe beneath the skirt to kick it out of the way. 'You are still very much overdressed,' he told her with mocking satire. 'Let us have the rest off!' His hands wandered, caressing, persuasively sensuous, while his lips tantalised her breasts. Tara clung to him, straining her body to his as a great yearning swelled within her, drawing her into the deluge of his pagan ardour. With a laugh of triumph he swung her up into his arms and carried her across the room. She watched him get undressed, every fibre of her being craving for his kisses, even though they were brutal, his arms, hard and cruel, his body, dominant and masterful, compelling hers to total and willing surrender.

## CHAPTER TWELVE

THE following morning, after Leon had questioned his wife and made no progress, he had the servants in one by one and as Tara expected the matter of the letter was brought to his notice.

'Who was it from?' he asked, but Tara would give nothing away. 'It was not from the post office, obviously,' he said grittingly.

'No, it was from the person who helped me.'

'And you are determined not to tell me who it is?' He was exceedingly puzzled, unable to understand how she could have got into touch with anyone outside the confines of the gardens. 'Some knavery has been going on under my very nose,' he said harshly, 'and I shan't rest until I've unravelled the mystery.' He looked at her. They were in the sitting-room, where he had interviewed all his servants. 'You do realise that an even closer watch will be kept on you from now on?'

She shrugged and said resignedly,

'I don't care any more, Leon. I'm your prisoner and I suppose there will be no escape for me for a very long time.' She sat there looking at him, remembering last night as she lay in his arms after the tumult of his passion had, as always, swept her to the very heights of bliss. Before, she had, after a while, wanted nothing more than to move away from him, to the other side of the bed. But last night everything seemed to have been different. Leon was more gentle for one thing, but it was not only that. She had *wanted* to remain in his arms, had no thought of shrinking from him and trying to move. She had revelled in the warmth and strength of his body long after the supreme moment was over. And this morning, when they had risen fairly late, she had wanted him to stay beside her, with his arms enclosing her, protectively.

'And I suppose you know too, that even if you make me that promise I shall not be able to trust you?'

Again she shrugged.

'I'll make the promise if you want me to,' she offered, 'and I'll keep it. However, if you can't trust me it's not a bit of use my making the promise. I shall have to live as I'm living now—as I've been living for weeks.' Tears started to her eyes and she swept an angry hand across them. 'What good are tears?' she said pettishly, talking to herself rather than to him.

'I don't like to see you cry,' he said.

'I didn't think it would affect you,' she returned, still in the same pettish voice.

He rose from his chair and went over to the window, his hands thrust deeply into the pockets of his slacks. She looked at his broad, straight back, noticing the tensed muscles through the cotton shirt he wore. Something stirred within her, a new and indefinable emotion. What was there about him that was different? Last night—or rather, in the early hours of this morning—she had almost fallen out of the bedroom window. She would have been killed at worst and badly injured at best. When first she had gained the advantage she had been in that state where she could have carried out her threat to jump. But later the very idea was terrifying and she knew she could not do it. However, by then she had realised that she had the whip hand anyway, since she only had to threaten and he would take notice. The result was the ultimatum, which he would have had to accept, letting her have her own way. Fate had intervened, sparing him the humiliation of defeat. She had believed that he would threaten her again, but instead he had made love to her. He had been afraid, she recalled, terribly afraid. . . . Did that fear mean more

than what she had concluded? She had believed that his
only reason for wanting her was desire. But that fear
—examined in retrospect—seemed to denote something
very different.

He turned to her at last and said,

'I feel that you will always try to escape me, Tara.'

She frowned at the flatness of his voice; it seemed
to her that a terrible dejection had him in its grip. 'You
see, I never really believed you would want to go.'

'You believed you held me by—by the physical pleasure you could give me?'

'Yes. I felt sure of it.' His eyes brooded as he sat down,
taking possession of the chair he had only a moment
ago vacated. He was restless, uncertain—not his usual
cool and superior self at all! No, there was a hint of
humility about him that staggered his wife. She found
she did not care for it in the least. It was out of character; she had become used to his mastery, which had
never failed to thrill her even while she fought against
it. Now there was something lacking in his make-up ...
something attractive ...? She glanced down at her
hand, clasped in her lap. Something was happening to
her, something vague but pleasant.

She said, in a quiet and sweetly gentle tone,

'I did say that physical compatibility isn't enough,
if you remember?'

'I remember,' he replied brusquely and without looking at her.

'There must be love in marriage,' she insisted.

'You were in love with David, or so you believed. Do
you really believe that, had you married him, you'd
both have remained blissfully happy for the rest of your
lives?'

'Yes, of course....' Her voice trailed away to a bewildered silence, for suddenly it seemed that she had
doubts, grave ones, regarding the future with David.

'Well?' The hard eyes were narrowed as they looked

intently into hers. 'You're not sure, is that it?'

Dazedly she shook her head, gazing at him in open wonderment, thunderstruck by the revelation that was slowly dawning in her mind. Impossible that she could be in love with *this monster*!—this pagan Greek who never missed an opportunity of showing her his mastery, of mocking her in that arrogant way of his that was designed—she was sure—to demonstrate his superiority over her.

'I—I am s-sure—yes!'

He laughed at her and said with a lift of his brows,

'Who are you trying to convince, Tara?' All the self-assurance was back and the hint of humility gone. This was the Leon she knew so well and had become used to ... and ... loved.....

No use denying it! She tried to shake it off, seeing life without him. Life would be good! Of course it would—with no one bossing her about, giving orders which she was compelled to obey. She would be free.... But did she want to be free? Life without him.... She closed her eyes, trying to shut out the bleak and lonely path which went endlessly on before her. The future, with *his memory* ever fresh and clear—— No! She was not so stupid as to have fallen in love with him. He was a brute and always would be.

'I'm *not* in love with him,' she cried silently over and over again. 'And even if I was,' she added inconsistently, 'I wouldn't want to stay with him, simply because of his beliefs that men in this part of the world are everything and women nothing!'

'I asked who you are trying to convince.' Her husband's voice came quietly and she raised her eyes, bewildered eyes and almost tearful. What upheavals there were in her life, and all on account of this man's criminal act in snatching her from the man she loved. Yes, it was David she loved! She had known it all the time. This husband of hers gave her only physical satis-

faction, but David could have given her that and
more important things besides.

'I know it's David I love, and I believe we would
have been happy all our lives.'

'Tell me about him?' A frown now to accompany
the words, and a return of that brooding, depressed
manner. 'What is he like in appearance?'

She told him, then explained all the things they had
had in common. She talked nostalgically about the
furnishing of the smart little house they had taken a
mortgage on. She talked of the thrill of waking up on
her wedding day and finding it was bright and sunny.

'My dress was beautiful——' She stopped and a
tear strayed through her long curling lashes to settle
on her pale cheek. She noticed the way Leon swallowed,
as if trying to remove something in his throat; and his
hands were clenching and unclenching—an uncon-
scious movement, she decided, to release some strong
and troublesome inner emotion. What was he thinking
about? Always she had found him inscrutable and he
was no different at this moment. 'You didn't think my
dress was beautiful,' she continued with a catch in her
voice, 'so you threw it in—in the sea.'

She did not mean it as a barb, or anything to hurt at
all . . . but to her astonishment she saw him wince.

'I think we shall change the subject,' he decided
shortly, and glanced at his watch. 'I shall have to work
in my study for the next couple of hours, but after that
I'll join you in the garden.'

He stood up; Tara lifted her head, tilting it right
back, and said after a small hesitation,

'Are you letting the matter drop—about my trying
to escape, I mean?'

The eyes, dark and intense, lingered on her face as
he replied,

'One day the truth will out, I suppose, but for
the present——' He flicked his hands, palms upwards.

'There doesn't seem anything to be gained by any more investing. I'm puzzled, naturally, because I am sure it wasn't one of the servants, and I don't know who you are acquainted with outside this house——' He stopped abruptly, his mouth going tight. He looked at her, looked directly into her eyes. 'Have you had a visitor while I've been away?' he demanded raspingly.

'A visitor?' she repeated, playing for time. She suspected at once whom he had in mind, because she had chatted with Nico for practically the whole time at the dinner party. 'Er—did you s-say a v-visitor——?'

'Nico!' he blazed. 'Nico was here, wasn't he!'

She shook her head, and at that moment she saw Elene sitting on the couch, pulling at a cigarette.

'Elene was here,' she told him, still playing for time and hoping this diversion would make him forget Nico.

'Elene?' he frowned. 'It was she who helped—— No, she couldn't have got that ladder up there!'

'What makes you suppose that Elene would help me to get away?' asked Tara with a sort of acid sweetness. 'Perhaps she would, though,' musingly and with a side-long glance at his chiselled face, which at present was like a thunder-cloud. 'It would serve her purpose to get me out of the way, wouldn't it, Leon? What was the quarrel about that made you throw her over and marry me on the rebound?'

He looked at her sharply.

'Did she tell you we had quarrelled?'

'Yes, she did.'

'What else did she tell you?' He was curious, and suddenly Tara was reluctant to have a discussion about the girl she had destested on sight.

'I'd rather not say. We'll let it drop, if you don't mind?'

'What reason did she give for coming?' he asked interestedly.

'She wanted to see you about something to do with

the coming fashion show in Athens. She was sorry she missed you. I expect she'll be getting in touch with you as soon as she knows you're back. Then you can question her as to what she told me.'

Leon's brows came together in a dark frown, but although he paused a moment as if he would question her further, he turned away eventually, and after saying it would be lunch time before he was with her, he went out, closing the door quietly behind him.

Another week went by, with life going on in the same dull manner. Tara wished she could see Nico, if only to tell him that Leon suspected him of helping her. She did not know that she could not have seen him anyway, because, after almost being caught red-handed placing that ladder, he had decided his presence could do no good now, so he had gone off, taking the boat out as usual, but sailing to the Greek island of Chios, where he had a friend who would not mind if he stayed for a week or two.

Leon had been very different during this time, and life had begun to settle into a rather pleasant routine for Tara. True, she still craved for escape, but she had to own that the imprisonment was becoming less and less irksome with every day that passed.

'Have you settled down?' her husband asked one day when they had—for the very first time—spent a pleasant hour together in the swimming-pool and were on the side, drying themselves. 'You seem more content.'

She looked at him keenly, responding to his smile and recalling the impression she had had that he might be coming to care for her ... or perhaps falling in love with her.

'I must admit I'm more content,' she answered, the desire strong within her to say what he wanted to hear, yet at the same time fully aware that if escape were to present itself at this moment she would not hesitate to grasp it.

'I'm glad, Tara.' His eyes were roving; she knew he was admiring her figure, her face and hair, and the lovely honey-peach tan she had acquired. 'Life could be good for us if you'd become resigned to being my wife—for ever.'

'And resigned to having you as my master?' she could not resist shooting at him. Leon frowned and drew a breath.

'I don't want to domineer over you,' he said unexpectedly. 'You goad me, Tara, and the worst of me comes out.'

She began drying her dainty toes with the towel, her mind confused, her heart throbbing wildly—for no apparent reason.

'It seems strange to hear that you've no wish to domineer over me, Leon.' Her beautiful blue eyes questioned him from their bewildered depths. 'Your actions and repeated threats don't tally at all with the statement you've just made.'

He nodded automatically, his forehead creased in a frown of deep concentration.

'You've driven me to those actions,' he began, but she could not help interrupting him before he went any further.

'I just resisted, when you were forcing your attentions on me! What else would you expect any woman to do?'

'You were my wife,' he reminded her with a hint of the imperiousness she knew so well. 'I had certain rights!'

Somehow, his words deflated her spirits and she felt a sense of loss which she could never have explained.

'I'm your wife by coercion,' she returned seriously. 'I don't know how you can say you have rights over me.'

'All men have rights over their wives.'

'Not all—no——' She shook her head vigorously. 'Only men who haven't advanced believe that.'

The dark pitchblende eyes smouldered, but only for a second.

'You're saying that I haven't advanced?' He seemed to give a sigh, she thought, and knew that it was his original intention to say something far stronger than that. She looked at him, seeing the brooding expression in his gaze, and feeling that he was by no means his usual assertive self. In fact, she had the firm impression that he was actually afraid of offending her.

'In many ways you're very Westernised,' she answered at length, 'but your attitude towards women and marriage is so outdated that the only chance of happiness for you is marriage to a Greek girl from one of the backward villages where the old customs and beliefs are still strong.' Her voice was low and serious, her eyes dark and faintly sad. She knew as she stared into his harsh pagan face that she loved him, that life with him could have been sheer bliss if only he knew what she desired, and gave it to her. Like many men he had separated love from sex, and like most men he could not understand why women could not do the same. Here was one of the greatest mysteries of nature—that men and women could think and feel so differently about something so vitally important to their happiness. A woman needed love to be the spur which sent her eagerly into a man's arms, and she wanted to know for sure that her love was returned.

Leon was speaking into her thoughts and this time there was a very noticeable harsh edge to his voice.

'As I'm already married there is no possibility of my marrying any Greek girl from one of these backward villages you mention.'

'You and I will never end our days together, Leon,' she told him sadly. A pause, but he did not speak. She said after a moment of considering, 'In ancient Japan it was recognised that a woman needed reassurance of love when she gave herself to a man, so it became the rule that the man would send the girl a token of love which she received the next morning, when she woke. If she did not receive this token, then there would never be a next time.'

Leon's eyes widened to their greatest extent.

'I don't believe it,' he declared.

Tara shrugged.

'I didn't think you would,' she returned, and there was such bitterness in her voice that it could not possibly escape him. He looked frowningly at her, appearing to be irritated by what she had said, and after a moment he got up, taking his towel, and walked away from her without uttering another word.

# CHAPTER THIRTEEN

Two days later Leon went down to the village to get his hair cut and to collect some clothes from Margarita. As she watched him go Tara recalled the story he had told to his servants as to why she must be watched all the time, and she concluded that he had given the same explanation to Margarita. Weeks were going by and very few people had seen Leon's new wife. Of course, it was not unusual for a Greek wife to stay at home the whole time, but for all that there must be a good deal of curiosity in the village. Leon had of course fully expected his wife to give him the promise, and the fact that she had not done so must by now be as embarrassing to him here, on the island, as it was in the capital, where his friends and business associates must be very puzzled indeed. Leon had obviously thought of something to put them off, but the present situation could hardly continue for ever. He was banking on her having a baby, and then she would be bound to him for a long, long while.

She wondered what his reaction would be when he learned that his hopes were to be dashed.

He had been gone less than half an hour when to her surprise she saw three men on donkeys coming up the path that led to the house. So few people came—— Her eyes suddenly dilated and she stood rooted to the spot, unable to believe what she saw; and she still could not believe it even when the name fell from her lips.

'David ...!' No, it could not be! She was dreaming —seeing things.

She managed to move, every nerve in her body quivering.

David here, and with two other men! Yes, they were real enough, and in other circumstances she could have laughed heartily at the way they were sitting astride the donkeys, looking as if they expected to fall off any second now. A long way behind them trailed the owner of the donkeys, the old man who made a living by hiring them out to tourists from the cruise ships. He had just tottered into view, a stick in his hand, his *vraga* dusty, and faded from black to a dull, patchy green.

'David,' she whispered again, the awareness that here was freedom scarcely registering in her bemused mind.

'Tara!' He had seen her and lifted a hand, then put it back on the donkey's neck with some considerable haste. She walked a few faltering steps, her legs like jelly, her mind chaotic. Leon would not return yet ... or would he? Obviously he had not see the men, down there on the harbour. He must have gone into the barber's shop only minutes before the men got off the ferry.

'David!' She found she could walk faster now, and then actually run. Davos was hurrying to the gate, but she was before him, opening it as the men dismounted. Within seconds David had her in his arms and she was crying against his chest. 'David,' she sobbed, 'oh, how did you know——? I mean, how can you be here!' Near hysteria spread over her, causing her body to shake. Freedom! Here without any doubts at all was freedom. Nothing could prevent her escape now, nothing or no one....

One of the men was a Greek, a plain-clothes policemen, the other was a plain-clothes English policeman who managed to convey this to her while she clung to David, his soothing words mingling with the business-like ones of the policemen.

Davos was standing by looking exceedingly troubled. Tara asked the English policemen to make him go away. However, Davos merely moved some small dis-

tance, then stopped, fingering a small branch of a
hibiscus bush as if he were considering doing something
to it, but all the while his dark Greek eyes were shift-
ing back and forth and it was plain that he was anxious
for Leon to come back.

'Can we go inside?' suggested the English policemen.
'Then we can begin to talk, and to sort this whole thing
out.'

The Greek moved over to speak to Davos in his own
language and Tara said again, looking up into David's
face,

'How do you come to be here? It's a miracle! I
couldn't believe it was you!'

'The police managed to get hold of a clue—after
weeks of drawing blank,' he told her, going on to explain that it was the porter who—having been off work
for several weeks—provided the clue when, after
making many other enquiries as to the people Tara
had mixed with, the police returned to the hospital to
ask more questions of the staff there. 'Tara darling, why
didn't you tell me that that damned fellow had sent you
flowers?'

'I couldn't—don't ask me why I should be so reluctant to tell you, David. I thought it would be less up-
setting all round if I just kept silent.'

'You also kept silent about the phone calls,' the
policeman inserted in tones of censure. 'If you'd told
someone we'd have had you back long ago.'

'The police followed up the clue provided by the
porter,' David explained. 'With that bit of information
they really got busy and the next thing was that the
telephone operator, reminded of the Greek, then recalled that a man with a slight foreign accent had been
trying to get you on the phone but you'd told her not
to put the calls through.' He paused and looked down
at her with the same expression of censure as the policeman had just a moment ago. 'You told the operator that

this man was making a nuisance of himself.'

She nodded and coloured guiltily.

'I should have confided in you, David, and I don't know why I didn't....' Her voice drifted away, her cheeks hot as she recalled the passionate interludes spent with the man who at that time was a stranger to her. It would have seemed odd indeed if she had complained to her fiancé that she was being pestered by a man, while at the same time participating willingly—eagerly—in the most ardent and intimate love-making with the man in question.

'If only you had, then he'd never have kidnapped you—you do realise that?'

She was silent, not at all sure of his confident assertion, because, knowing her husband so well, she certainly would never take bets on his failing to do what he set out to do.

The Greek policeman—who had been introduced to her by David as Phivos Meriakis—returned with the information that Davos was as uncommunicative as a deaf mute.

'Scared of his employer,' he added in a disgusted and strongly accented voice. 'I've scared him, though!'

They all went into the house and once in the cool and restful atmosphere of the sitting-room, Tara felt more calm, more able to appreciate what had happened. She was able to consider her situation, to savour the knowledge that her husband's tryanny was finished, that he could no longer hold her prisoner. She was able also to answer coherently the questions put to her both by the Greek policeman and by Oscar Stewart, the English policeman. David sat forward on his chair, listening, and Tara heard a little groan issue from his lips when he learned of the ultimatum put to her by Leon, and of the choice she had made.

'So you're married? Oh, God, the swine!'

'It was marriage or the other, as I've just said.' She

could have wept for the misery she saw in David's honest, English face. 'You must surely have known that I'd be in a horrible position?'

'I didn't dare think about it,' he shuddered. 'I've been through hell with my imagination!' Another shiver passed through him and for a space he obviously found it impossible to form words. 'I tried not to think that anything abominable could happen to the girl I loved.' His voice seemed to draw away slowly, and as she watched his face with a strange indefinable fascination she saw the change in his expression as a look of distaste replaced the unhappiness.

It would seem that he could hardly bear the thought that another man had owned her. It was an understandable emotion, Tara admitted, and yet....

'Married,' he was murmuring to himself, 'married to another man, and a foreigner.... Another man doing that to her——' Abruptly he snapped off his words, and colour fused his cheeks.

'You could never forget that I've been married to someone else?' she asked him curiously. An odd unfathomable sensation had come to her, bringing doubts that were as inexplicable as they were hazy. She had loved her fiancé dearly at the time of the abduction, and for a few highly emotional and grateful seconds out there just now, in the garden, she had believed she loved him still. But what of her husband? She had admitted that she loved *him* ... and it was not possible to love two men.

'I—I—— Oh, hell, Tara,' he exploded, wiping the sweat from his brow, 'don't ask me questions like that at present! I can't think straight——'

'But you must have been prepared for something like this?' interrupted Tara gently. 'I'd been abducted— and no girl's abducted for nothing. The man who abducted me had designs on me——'

'Be quiet, Tara!'

'Can we get on to something more important?' suggested Oscar Stewart impatiently. 'Where is your husband now?'

'He's out, in the village.'

'We want him for questioning.'

'How did you find him?' asked Tara curiously.

'Easy. Through Interpol.'

'Interpol....' The very word was hateful to her, bringing her husband into the category of a criminal.

'I'd like to ask you more questions while we wait for your husband to come back.' It was the English policeman, Oscar Stewart, who spoke, and she gave him her whole attention. 'You obviously married Mr Petrides willingly. What I can't understand is why you didn't enlist help from the man who married you?'

'Yes,' interposed David, 'why didn't you? You could have done, surely?'

She explained everything from beginning to end and even before she had finished the Greek policeman was shaking his head.

'There's no case against him,' he began, when Oscar Stewart interrupted him.

'There was an abduction, and it took place in England——'

'An abduction with intent to marry,' interrupted the Greek. 'In any case, this young woman cannot give evidence against her husband.'

Oscar Stewart's mouth went tight; that he was angry was evident. As for Tara's reaction ... well, she hadn't for one moment relished the idea of her husband being taken to England under arrest. Of course, he must always have known that even if the matter did happen to be carried that far, she would not be able to give evidence against him, for that was the law. Something in her expression must have caught David's attention— perhaps her relief that there would be no case against her husband—for he said, staring at her in some perplexity,

'You—still love me?' The hesitant start convinced her that he had re-phrased the original question that had come to his lips. He had intended asking if she was in love with her husband.

'All I want at present, David,' she returned frankly, 'is to get away from here, back to England, where I can begin getting over the ordeal.'

'I understand, darling. Well, we can take you away at once.'

She gave him a smile, reflecting on those occasions when his endearments thrilled her and when she had never believed the day would dawn when they would leave her cold, as his use of the endearment did at this moment.

If only Leon had used it.... He would not know how! She felt sure he had never used the word darling in the whole of his life.

'How long will Mr Petrides be?' the Greek policeman wanted to know. 'Although there's no case, we shall have to ask him a few questions, and then tell him we're taking you away.' He paused, looking directly at her through faintly narrowed eyes. 'You're sure you want to leave him?' he asked, and David gave a start, at the same time uttering an angry exclamation.

'Certainly she wants to leave him! Hasn't she already made that quite clear?'

Tara rose from her chair, offering to get the men some refreshment. Oscar Stewart wanted a cup of tea, while his Greek counterpart asked for *ouzo* and a *mezé*. David had a stronger drink—a brandy.

These were brought by Stamati, who had obviously been told about the visitors by Davos, because he was looking extremely worried.

'Why don't you go and pack your clothes?' suggested David. 'We don't want to miss the next ferry and have to spend the night at the hotel down there, on the quay.'

She looked at him, frowning at the idea of spending the night at the hotel when her husband's house was here. It was stupid, and yet surely she wanted to get away with all speed, shake the soil of that garden off her heels? There had been many lonesome hours spent out there—a prisoner, constantly watched. And now she was free to leave it all and return to her own country. She found herself thinking of the hospital, and of all the gossip there would be, and she decided she could never go back, nor could she take up with David again. What would she do, then? As before—and as she had just mentioned to David—she resolved to take first things first; she would get away from here and then sort out plans for her future.

# CHAPTER FOURTEEN

IT seemed impossible that her husband could put fear into her at a time like this, when she had the protection of three men, two of whom were from her own country. And yet there was a most uncomfortable feeling in the pit of her stomach when, from the window of the sitting-room, she saw Leon crossing the lawn. In his hand was a large cardboard box, the contents of which would have been exciting to most women.

Davos ran to him; she saw him stiffen, dart a glance towards the window, then come forward again with much longer strides than before. Well, *he* obviously had no fear within him—but then she had known he would accept the present situation in a way that, at first, could possibly disconcert the enemy.

He strode in, his tall figure towering above those of the other three men, all of whom had risen from their chairs. Leon was soon told who they were and the nature of their business. Watching him intently, Tara never once saw any sign that he was anxious or apprehensive. His eyes were continually finding hers while the two policemen talked to him, but on a couple of occasions Leon's black eyes became fixed on David's pale face, and a sneer would settle on his own. How confident he was! Tara could not stem the flow of pride that this confidence brought to her. It would seem that whatever the circumstances he would ride them with all the supreme arrogance of the pagan gods which his ancestors had worshipped.

When the two men had finished speaking—and asking questions which Leon had answered either in monosyllables or not at all—he looked at his wife and said,

'Apparently you have told these men that you married me willingly?'

'Yes, I have.' She looked away without knowing why, for there was neither censure nor arrogance in his expression—on the contrary, there did seem to be a hint of sadness in his eyes. Perhaps it was this which she just had to avoid.

'In which case, you have absolutely nothing to complain about?'

'She has a hell of a lot to complain about!' shouted David hotly. 'Your damned treatment of her in taking her off on the day of her wedding—only an hour or so before she was to have been married to me!'

The tall lithe frame swung round.

'Tara promised to marry me long before her wedding day,' he informed him calmly. 'She jilted me to marry you, which I could not accept. She knows in her heart that I did the right thing in carrying her off——'

'She was engaged to you!' David looked from the dark face of the man who had stolen his bride, to the face of the girl herself. It was fused with crimson colour, and tiny beads of perspiration stood out on her temples. 'This isn't true! It can't possibly be—I'd never heard of this man until you mentioned his being in hospital!'

'Is this true?' from Oscar Stewart with a deep frown.

'You were engaged?' intervened the Greek policeman, shaking his head. 'If this is correct then——' He broke off and shrugged heavily. 'In Greece an engagement is almost the marriage. It is never broken—or almost never broken,' he amended, after a swift moment of thought.

'I was never engaged to Mr Petrides,' said Tara in a stiff little voice which was nothing like her own.

'I didn't mention the word engaged.' Leon looked at her, and when she lowered her head he had the arrogance to step forward and, in front of them all, jerk her head up with a possessive hand under her chin. 'You promised to marry me.' So slow the words, and challenging. A thrill of apprehension rippled along her spine. 'I assume you are not going to lie, wife! Did you or did you not promise to marry me?' He was towering above her, a menacing figure with whom none of the three men seemed inclined to interfere as he gave his wife's chin another jerk, just to remind her that he expected an immediate answer to his question.

'Yes—yes, I d-did promise to—to m-marry you,' she admitted chokingly.

'You couldn't have——!' David was shaking his head dazedly. 'What the hell's going on?' he demanded of Leon. 'How long have you known her?'

'We met when he was in hospital,' said Tara, white to the lips and wishing she could escape to some quiet spot and collect herself, restore her jagged nerves. 'He believed we—we were meant for one another, and he did convince me at one time that he and I were—were suited——'

'When was this, for God's sake?'

'About a week before the date arranged for your wedding,' answered Leon suavely and with a glance of amused satire thrown in his wife's direction. 'She promised to give you up and marry me.'

'It's ... impossible,' protested David. 'Tara, say it. Deny it all——'

'She can't,' interrupted her husband, walking away and standing with his back to the window. 'She has just admitted that she promised to marry me. She did marry me, willingly, and we're expecting our first child——'

'No!' David started forward, then stopped, raising a hand viciously as if he would have liked to strike the man standing there by the window, a look of arrogant mockery in his gaze. 'Tara, you're not——' Suddenly he seemed to sag, and he found a chair and sank into it.

Looking from his shrunken figure to that of her husband Tara could not help comparing the two and finding her former fiancé greatly wanting. And yet pity in abundance filled her heart, because he had loved her dearly, and even though she was convinced that he could never have picked up the threads any more than she, there was no doubt in her mind that he was suffering agonies from what had happened. She said quietly, looking at her husband,

'It so happens that I am not expecting a child. My husband has made a mistake there,' she added, transferring her gaze to David.

Leon's glance was sharp, piercing and disbelieving.

'Is this right?' he demanded.

'There is nothing to bind me to you, Leon,' was her soft and sad reply. 'So I'm leaving with these men on the next ferry. If you'll excuse me——?' She looked around, her glance embracing them all. 'I'll go and pack for the journey and I'll be down in less than fifteen minutes.'

'Tara—wait!' The command was snapped out imperiously from her husband. 'You are not leaving me, do you hear?'

'There's nothing to stop her coming with us.' Oscar Stewart spoke at last, in firm and even tones. 'You took her away illegally, and——'

'Would you make charges against me?' broke in her husband, eyeing her curiously.

'I....' Her voice faltered. She would have liked to give him a few moments of anxiety, but she could not stand here and tell him she would charge him when she had no intention of doing any such thing.

The merest hint of a taunting smile hovered on his lips as he said,

'You have often said you would like to see me in jail, my dear. Are you still of the same mind?'

'It would be what you deserve.'

'You haven't answered my question.'

'I shall not charge you with anything,' she returned quietly, and heard an angry exclamation escape from Oscar Stewart's lips.

'So you are not now of the same mind?' Leon's smile was withdrawn and his whole manner became serious. 'No?'

'Time has passed since I said those words. I no longer want to see you in jail.'

'Then there's no need for any questioning, even,' decided Phivos Meriakis. 'This lady promised to marry him, then changed her mind and went off to marry someone else. It seems to me that she does not know which one she wants. In Greece she would be called fickle and no man would look at her. She would have to be a single lady all her life.'

Tara flushed, aware of Leon's laughing eyes fixed upon her. There was an audacious, devil-may-care attitude about him which Tara found extraordinarily attractive—although not for one moment would she have admitted it.

'I'm going to pack,' she said, and went out before Leon could utter another command. But within three minutes of her reaching her bedroom he was there, standing in the doorway between the two rooms, one hand resting carelessly on the jamb, the other thrust into the pocket of his blazer-type jacket.

'What do you want?' She had to speak, to break the silence, which frightened her, since it seemed like the calm before the storm. Even now she was scared of him, terribly afraid that, somehow, he could prevent her from getting away.

'Is it true that you're not pregnant?' Soft the words and challenging. She would not have dared to lie to him.

'Yes, it's true. For once fate has been kind to me.' She had a suitcase on the bed and was absently throwing things into it from a drawer in the dressing-table. 'I'm free at last, Leon, so you've lost the last round.'

'I never admit defeat, Tara.'

'This time you'll have to.' A pair of tights and an underslip were tossed into the case. 'I'll send all these back to you later—in the suitcase——'

'Shut up!'

She swallowed, wishing her heart would not throb so.

'What are the policemen doing?' she asked, just for something to say.

'I have no idea. Arguing, I shouldn't wonder. Your Englishman's mad that he can't arrest me.'

'I wouldn't have had you arrested.' She turned to take more underwear from the drawer.

'Why?' queried her husband briefly, and disconcertingly.

'I don't bear a grudge to that extent.' A nightgown was bundled into the suitcase and then she closed the drawer and stood still, a terrible depression flooding over her. From outside came the trilling of cicadas, and the happy song of a bird. What drew her to the window she never knew. Perhaps she wanted to take one last look at the water over which she would be sailing before another couple of hours had passed.

Her husband said,

'Come here, Tara.'

She shook her head and went to one of the wardrobes, from where she took out a dress and a coat, putting the former into the case and the latter on the end of the bed. As she turned Leon was there, towering above her, close—oh, so close that there was no possibility of escape! His arms were painful in their strength, and so were his sensuous lips. Her quivering mouth parted at his command and his lips tantalised, sending ripples along her spine, awakening desires already.

'You can't leave me,' he stated confidently. 'You're

mine, Tara—my possession! I shall never let you go—never!'

'Nothing you can do now can keep me here,' she managed to say before her lips were crushed again, with unbridled brutality this time.

'By God, but you do try me! Do you suppose I shall allow my wife to leave me—to go off with another man——!'.

'Another man?' she repeated, staring at him.

'That jellyfish cowering down there in a chair! He's not for you, you little fool! You need a *man*! You need me!'

'I need neither of you!' she flashed, managing with a supreme effort—and the advantage of surprise—to free herself from the savage grip of his hands. 'I shall never marry—if that's any consolation to you!'

'You are married.'

'In a few months' time I won't be!' Running to the bed, she closed the lid of the case and snapped the two locks. She picked up the coat, throwing it over one arm, and took up the case with the other. When she turned Leon was barring her way. A sort of terror filled her and she let out a piercing scream.

'You blasted——' Leon stopped at the sound of footsteps racing up the stairs. The door crashed open and the three men crowded through the doorway into the room.

'What's wrong?' David, his face a greyish mask, put the question to her and for answer she passed the case into his hand.

'Take me away,' she sobbed, her nerves shattered, her heart hammering painfully, loudly, against her ribs. 'I want to go back to England!'

Leon seemed uncertain, and for a moment Tara thought he would do battle with the three men standing there. But at last it seemed to register that, strong as he was, he could never be a match for three men, plus any help which she might decide to give.

'This isn't the end. You'll be back!' Her husband's confident assertion was the last thing she heard as, turning, she left the room, followed by David and the two policemen.

She was on the boat when David said, avoiding her gaze,

'That man has some influence over you, hasn't he?'

She nodded, unwilling to lie. In any case, there was no need.

'Yes, David, it was apparent from the moment I saw him in that hospital ward.'

'Yet you said nothing to me.'

'It wasn't the sort of thing one talked about,' she returned reasonably, and with a hint of apology.

'You tried to shake off the influence?'

'Of course. I wanted nothing more than to marry you.' Her eyes wandered to where the two policemen stood by the rail. Phivos Meriakis was going back to Athens, and Oscar Stewart to England. He was furious with her, having believed he would have a case against her husband. Of course, there would have been a case —a serious one—if Leon had not married her.

'But you don't want to marry me now?' David was saying.

'*You* don't want to marry *me*,' she challenged, and saw him nod. 'It would have been a mistake, although at the time we truly believed we were made for each other.' He said nothing and she added, in that low sweet voice he had once loved so well, 'It's sad, David, but better for us to have found out beforehand, isn't it?'

He frowned and answered in a pained tone of voice,

'If that swine hadn't carried you off we'd have been married, and I feel sure we'd have been happy.'

'For a time—yes. I'm as sure of it as you are. But, later, it would have gone wrong, David.'

'How can you say that?'

'Because we've both discovered that we don't love one another.'

He made no denial, but gave a small sigh instead.

'Let's go and have a meal in the restaurant,' he suggested. 'It'll be the last one we shall have together,' he added on a bitter note, and it was Tara's turn to sigh; but she agreed to have the meal and they went off, leaving the two policemen standing by the rail, chatting together.

It was arranged that Tara, David and Oscar Stewart would fly to England together, but when Oscar Stewart made enquiries about a flight he was told that all seats on the evening flight were booked, and even on the following day there was only one seat available.

'It means we'll have to put up at an hotel,' growled Oscar, still furious that he had not managed to get a case. 'More waste of time!'

'We might as well see something of the city,' Tara suggested to David. 'Let's go up to the Acropolis.'

Reluctantly he agreed; it was a sombre interlude and long before they returned to the hotel Tara was wishing she had gone on her own.

'I believe you're glad we can't fly back to England at once,' said David sourly as they wandered across the site, making their exit.

'That's a silly thing to say.'

'I don't think so. You seem to me as if you're glad you're still in Greece—*his* country!' She sighed and said nothing and after a pause he went on, 'He still exerts his influence over you, even though he's miles away. Are you sure you're not in love with him?' he added with a hint of scorn. And there was a sneer on his lips, the first she had seen since she had known him—and she could not blame for it.

'If you must know,' she replied frankly, 'I am in love with him.'

'I knew it!' The contempt spread to his eyes. 'Why, then, are you running from him? It's plain that you enjoy being domineered—— God, the way he handled you—pushing your face up like that! Yet you never murmured one word of protest, Tara. What kind of a woman are you?'

'I don't know,' broodingly and almost to herself. 'Leon's personality is so strong that—that I feel sort of —helpless——'

'And like it? The he-man appeal, eh? And how long will a girl like you tolerate being subjugated by a damned foreigner?'

'It's because I object to being subjugated that I'm leaving him,' she returned. 'I should have thought you'd have guessed that, seeing that you guessed I love him.' She was pale but composed, accepting with a sort of agonised resignation that she and Leon could never live together again. If only he had loved her. . . . If only he could be masterful without being cruel. . . . If only he could make love with respect and tenderness. . . .

Life for her without those things that really mattered had been unbearable. Leon was from the East, a man whose attitude towards the women in his life—be they wife, daughter or anyone else—was that of arrogant domination. His word was law and never could it be argued with; his will was supreme; his orders had to be obeyed without question. And so, much as she loved him, Tara was resigned never to setting eyes on him again.

That evening David was so objectionable with her that she suggested he take the one available seat on the following day's flight and leave her to travel later with the policeman. He agreed. It was an awkward goodbye and when it was over and David had gone she felt utterly drained. And Oscar Stewart did not help when, as they were having dinner, he made no pretence at civility.

'All this waiting's a damned waste of time!' he declared. 'I wouldn't have minded if I could have taken that husband of yours back with me! We never thought that he'd have married you! That's what made a mess of the whole bl—— the whole damned business!'

Tara's chin lifted at his manner.

'I'm glad there isn't a case!' she snapped.

'Are you in love with the rogue?' he asked belligerently. 'If you are then what are you doing here?'

'I don't know....' She looked at him, still angry but aware that tears were pressing against her eyes.

'You don't know?' His manner changed dramatically. 'You must know! You *are* in love with him!'

Ignoring that, Tara brushed a hand across her eyes and said, 'You keep on about losing a case, but I'll tell you this, Mr Stewart: there never could have been a case simply because I'd have saved my husband from prosecution by saying I went with him willingly, that I was not kidnapped at all!'

'You——!' He stared at her. 'Do you suppose anyone would have believed you? You were on your way to a wedding, remember—your own wedding!' She had no comment to make and after a while he went on wrathfully, 'Women! Perverse creatures, all of them. They don't know their own minds for five minutes at a time! You say you want to get back to England, but it strikes me it's your abductor you want to get back to!'

She looked down at her plate, avoiding that strange expression that had settled on his face. He could almost have been planning something, she thought. And how right he was when he stated that she wanted to go back to her husband. She admitted it to herself freely now, and yet she said,

'We fly home tomorrow? You're sure you have the seats booked?'

'I've a good mind to let you make your own way.' Fury in his tone and yet another edge to it which she failed to comprehend. And he was still staring strangely at her when at last she glanced up.

'You wouldn't do that,' she returned confidently. 'You wouldn't leave me here, on my own.'

'No,' he murmured, his voice surprisingly mellowed. 'No, I wouldn't leave you here alone. . . .'

The following morning Tara went out into the city streets, wandering along from place to place and ending up in Constitution Square where she had a cup of coffee at an outdoor *cafeneion*. After that she decided to go to the Acropolis again, where she knew she could find peace, if only for a little while. She wandered about the ruins, trying to visualise what the site was like in those ancient days when all the marble buildings were in pristine condition, and the crowds would congregate her to pay homage to the pagan goddess Athena.

The time wore on, and it was hunger that made her suddenly realise that the sun was going down and that soon the city of Athens would be 'violet-crowned'.

She had scarcely entered the lobby of the hotel when she heard her name spoken and she spun around to come face to face with Nico.

'What are you doing here?' he asked, and although there was an odd inflection in his tone it did not register with her. 'Is—is Leon with you?'

She shook her head.

'I've escaped, Nico,' she said, and her voice was very flat.

'Escaped? You managed it—but how?' He seemed to be taking it too calmly, she thought, but before she had time to answer his question he was suggesting they go to the lounge and talk over a drink. Once there, Tara

wasted no time in explaining everything to him, and
after that he was doing some explaining himself, telling
her how he had had to race away from that ladder because he knew that if Leon had seen him he would most
certainly have caught him.

'He can run faster than I,' he ended ruefully.

'I don't blame you for running away, but why didn't
you get in touch with me later?'

'I thought I'd better disappear for a while, just in
case it should occur to Leon that it was I who was helping you.'

It *had* occurred to Leon, but to Tara's surprise he
had not pursued the matter. It now occurred to her that
he must have tried to find Nico, but Nico had prud-
ently gone off, putting himself out of his reach.

'And why are you here now?' she wanted to know.

There was a slight hesitation before Nico answered,
and when he did answer he seemed to be deliberately
avoiding her eyes.

'I have my boat at Piraeus.'

'And are you returning to Hydra soon?'

'Yes, quite soon.' He looked at her questioningly.
'You'd like to come back to Hydra?'

She shook her head, but did wonder if it was convincing.

'Are you in love with Leon, Tara?' The question
came after a long silence, and it seemed that Nico had
some difficulty in asking it.

She looked at him through misty eyes, swallowing
hard and wishing their drinks would come so that she
could ease this dryness in her throat.

'Yes,' she owned simply, 'I am in love with Leon. But
I can't stay, Nico,' she went on sadly, 'because I'm
English and I want my husband to love me. In Greece
it's almost always a loveless marriage—or it can be one-
sided, I suppose, simply because women the world over
seem to fall in love——' Bitterness edged her voice as

she thought again of the vagaries of nature in creating conflicting emotions in men and women. 'I'm English,' she said again, 'and I must have love in my marriage, love from my husband.'

'You sound very sad about it all,' he said, a distinct catch in his voice.

'Of course I'm sad.' She looked into his dark face, into his eyes, aware of their odd expression but naturally attaching no significance to it. 'What woman wouldn't be sad at having to desert the husband she loves? My life would be bliss if Leon loved me. Yes, of course I'm sad,' she repeated, and it was with the greatest difficulty that she held back the tears that had gathered behind her eyes.

'I could have liked you a lot myself, but there was never any chance for me. I see that now.'

'It was kind of you to offer to help me to escape, Nico.'

'I didn't do much good. Was Leon mad?'

'Don't ask me about it,' she shuddered. 'I thought he'd murder me!'

'He always did have a temper.' He looked at her and a thin smile touched his lips. 'He always attracted the women, too. Nice gentle men like me are not greatly in demand.'

'One day, Nico, you'll find the right one.'

He shrugged and changed the subject.

'Elene's leaving Hydra and living permanently in Athens.'

'She is?' Tara's heart fluttered. 'So the affair between Leon and her won't be resumed?'

Nico shook his head.

'It's over. Leon's married now, remember.' Strange his tone and puzzling. 'Greek people consider that marriage is for ever.'

'I'm intending to divorce him,' she said, and once again her voice was very flat.

The drinks arrived and she took a larger gulp than ever before. People often drowned their sorrows in drink, she thought, and almost wished she could do the same. Unfortunately there was always the awakening.

'He won't be happy about a divorce——' Nico stopped abruptly and frowned. 'Let's have a change of subject——' He took a quick glance at his watch as if an idea had just come to him. 'You're not flying until midnight, you said?'

'That's right—if that policeman takes me, which I hope he does.'

'Look, would you care to have a couple of hours on my boat?'

'I've to be at the airport at a quarter to eleven,' she said doubtfully. 'I wouldn't have time. I must be here, waiting, when Mr Stewart is ready to leave.' She shook her head decisively. 'It would have been nice, Nico, but I haven't eaten yet——'

'We could have something on the boat. I had intended having my dinner here, but we could knock up something on the boat. My crew are rather good at that sort of thing.' He was eager, waiting for her answer. She would rather not take any risks, just in case something happened and she missed the plane. However, it would obviously be a disappointment to Nico if she refused his offer, and she found herself accepting it with a smile.

They took a taxi to the port, and soon Tara was boarding the luxury yacht. It reminded her of Leon's graceful vessel ... and of the fear she had known when being forced aboard.

'Carry on into the saloon,' Nico was saying. 'I'll be back in a minute.' She turned and he was gone. Where was the saloon? At least he could have taken her there before going off like that. Why was it so dark ... this boat——

'Good evening, Tara.' The suave half-mocking voice

slashed at her thoughts and she spun round, every vestige of colour draining from her face. 'So I kidnap you for the second time—with the assistance of my good friend Nico.' He was standing there, in a doorway, so casual, so confident. 'I must say that it becomes a little boring, having to repeat this performance. Put me to the trouble a third time and I shan't be responsible for my actions. Come here!'

Instead she turned, with the intention of either getting off the boat or jumping into the water, as it would be easy to swim to safety. But she was caught by the hand and prevented from doing anything except look up into her husband's dark face ... and gasp at what she saw there.

'This boat's yours,' was all she could find to say before his lips came down to meet hers, and his kiss was infinitely tender.

'Darling, I couldn't help teasing you just now, but it wasn't worth it after all; you looked so frightened. Don't ever be afraid of me again, my dear, dear love....' His voice trailed to a husky silence and it seemed that words failed him for a while because he just held her close to his heart so that she heard its wild beating high above her own. Dazedly she thought: the miracle's happened. And how it had happened was by no means important, she knew, but such were her emotions that she found herself gripping the lapels of his coat with frenzied fingers and saying wildly,

'I'm so confused—— Oh, Leon, how did it happen! I can't believe it's true—tell me it's true,' she cried, the tears actually starting to her eyes. 'You—love m-me?'

'I adore you!' He caught her to him again and for the next few moments Tara found herself being carried on the tide of his ardour as she had on so many occasions before. But this time it was different ... because he loved her.

'How did it happen?' she asked again when at last he released her.

He led her into the saloon and put on a few shaded lights. It was a romantic setting for his explanation, with the dimmed lights and flowers and the gentle sway of the boat. And as if that were not enough there drifted from somewhere along the waterfront the haunting strains of music being played by a *bouzouki* band.

Tara and Leon sat side by side on a couch, fingers entwined, and he began to talk. She learned many things as she listened, her head on his shoulder—learned of his sheer terror when she sat on that windowsill, learned that his subsequent fury was the result of that fear. He then told her of his determination to tackle Nico on his return from Chios, of how he had forced the truth from him, telling him he would have done him, Leon, a bad turn if his help had proved successful, because he loved his wife.

Leon then went on to give her the surprising news that Oscar Stewart had thought fit to telephone him with the information that Tara would have lied rather than have a case brought against her husband.

'When he said that you'd have insisted that you came with me willingly I knew that you loved me—the fact that you would lie to save me proved it.' He took her tenderly to his breast, kissing her quivering lips. 'My darling, I'd hoped that you would come to love me, but I'd treated you so badly——' He stopped, and a sigh of deep regret escaped him. 'I never wanted to fall in love,' he admitted frankly, 'and I secretly derided your sentiments about loving and caring being so important that there could be no happiness in marriage without them. But in the end, my love, I came to accept your wisdom without question. And if there were any doubts left in my mind they were gone that night when you nearly fell.' He seemed to shudder and it was with a sort of joyous wonderment that Tara saw how deeply he was affected by what had happened. 'As I said, I wanted your love, but I was always conscious of what I'd done to you in the beginning——'

'But you said it was for the best, and it was,' she broke in, snuggling close against his breast.

'Perhaps it was wishful thinking,' he admitted unexpectedly. 'To be honest, darling, I was afraid—dreadfully afraid, once I began to realise that I loved you.' He paused, but she said nothing and he proceeded to tell her how he had asked Nico to accompany him to Piraeus, and they had planned for Nico to stay in the hotel until he came across Tara.

'But why didn't you come yourself, Leon?' she asked, puzzled.

'Because,' he answered wryly, 'I feared that if you only so much as set eyes on me you'd turn and run and never stop until you were exhausted. Then I'd have had to go to a lot of trouble to find you again. No, it was easier——'

'You'd have found me?' she said, and instantly his brows lifted and in his voice when he answered she recognised all the old familiar mastery.

'I should have found you all right. Haven't I said that I shall never let you go—that you are mine, for ever!'

'Yes, Leon,' she returned in a low tone, 'you have.'

'As I was saying, it was easier to do it the way we have, with Nico inviting you on to my boat.'

'He was very convincing; he didn't give a thing away.'

'I told him to be careful. It would have been frustrating if you'd refused to come aboard the boat.'

'Nico must have felt obligated to you,' murmured Tara mechanically.

'He was less willing than you've assumed. He said he'd help me but that he would not entice you aboard unless he was sure that you loved me. *My* loving *you* wasn't enough for him, he said. He'd be a traitor to you if he brought you aboard and you didn't want to

come back to me. It would, in effect, be condemning
you to imprisonment, as he called it—which sounds
very much like the phrasing my wife has used on more
than one occasion,' added Leon with a hint of amusement.

'I realise now that Nico did ask some rather pointed
questions,' she told him musingly. 'Yes, he made sure
he knew I loved you before he asked me to come on to
*his* boat!'

'Well, he had to say it was his, hadn't he?'

'Oh, Leon, I do love him for what he did!'

Her husband held her from him.

'You what!'

'You know what I mean,' she laughed. 'I love you too,
of course.'

'Thanks for those kind words! I shall require them to
be far more romantically put later, after we have eaten
a very special dinner that is being prepared for us.'

'Nico said his crew would manage to get something
together!'

'All part of the deception. And it worked!' He drew
her close, his hard lips crushing hers beneath them and
never drawing away until she was gasping for breath.

'When did you know you were falling in love with
me?' Tara wanted to know when she had recovered.

'That is a question I find it impossible to answer.'
The black eyes looked into hers for a long moment and
then, 'I often wonder if it was love at first sight,' he
admitted reflectively, 'because never in my life have I
been so greatly attracted to a woman as I was to you
when we met in that hospital ward. I wanted you, and I
vowed to have you.'

She just shook her head in wonderment. It had never
occurred to either of them that it could have been love
at first sight.

'I thought it was desire, Leon,' she said.

'So did I, at the time, but. . . .' He shrugged and said

it really made no difference because he loved her now.

'I do remember that I was blazing mad when you mentioned pillow-friends,' he mused. 'I knew even then that I would never have another as long as I lived, and that was what inflamed me when you talked about them. I must have been in love with you from very early on,' he added with a wry smile.

'There was a time when I thought you might be falling in love with me, Leon, but afterwards I felt I was mistaken.'

'It was a pity that neither of us spoke about our feelings. I must have known that love was dawning with you as well, because you are not the girl to give herself freely just for desire.' He sounded contrite and she turned her face to his and her lips were soft and yielding on his mouth. 'God, but I love you!' he said hoarsely, bringing her slender body against the iron-hard muscles of his own. He stood up, bringing her with him, but he just held her then in a gentle tender embrace and looked down into her big blue eyes, eyes filled with love and happiness. There were a few explanations still to be made, but neither felt inclined to waste any more time on such things now. And so they just stood there, in the shaded light of the saloon, their bodies close, their thoughts on the future and the joys of loving and caring which were, after all, the most important things in marriage.

## The Mills & Boon Rose is the Rose of Romance

Every month there are ten new titles to choose from — ten new stories about people falling in love, people you want to read about, people in exciting, far away places. Choose Mills & Boon. It's your way of relaxing.

### May's titles are:

**PAGAN LOVER** by Anne Hampson
Tara had been forced to marry the masterful Leon Petrides and there was no escape — but did she really want to get away?

**GARDEN OF THORNS** by Sally Wentworth
Somebody was trying to get rid of Kirsty, but she just *couldn't* believe it was the autocratic Squire, Gyles Grantham.

**KELLY'S MAN** by Rosemary Carter
Kelly found it very galling that, despite all her efforts, Nicholas Van Mijden should still persist in thinking of her as just a spoiled rich girl.

**DEBT OF DISHONOUR** by Mary Wibberley
Renata's job was to look after a difficult teenage girl — but she found the girl's forbidding uncle more difficult and unpredictable to deal with!

**CRESCENDO** by Charlotte Lamb
'If you let them, women will take you over completely,' was Gideon Firth's philosophy — and that philosophy had ruined Marina's life.

**BAY OF STARS** by Robyn Donald
Bourne Kerwood had been described as 'a handsome bundle of dynamite' — and that dynamite had exploded all over Lorena's young life!

**DARK ENCOUNTER** by Susanna Firth
'For the salary you're offering I'd work for the devil himself' — and when Kate started work for Nicholas Blake she soon began to wonder if that wasn't just what she *was* doing ...

**MARRIAGE BY CAPTURE** by Margaret Rome
Married against her will, Claire promised herself that the marriage would be in name only — but that promise was a surprisingly difficult one to keep!

**BINDABURRA OUTSTATION** by Kerry Allyne
'Go back to the city where you belong,' ordered Kelly Sinclair contemptuously, and Paige would have been only too glad to oblige — but fate forestalled her ...

**APOLLO'S DAUGHTER** by Rebecca Stratton
Bethany resented Nikolas Meandis when he tried to order her life for her — and that was before she realised just what he was planning for her ...

If you have difficulty in obtaining any of these books from your local paperback retailer, write to:

Mills & Boon Reader Service
P.O. Box 236, Thornton Road, Croydon, Surrey, CR9 3RU.

# The Mills & Boon Rose is the Rose of Romance

## Look for the Mills & Boon Rose next month

**JACINTHA POINT** *by Elizabeth Graham*
To save her father, Laurel had been forced to marry the masterful Diego Ramirez, a man she did not know and certainly did not love.

**FUGITIVE WIFE** *by Sara Craven*
Briony had no doubts about her love for Logan Adair. Yet their marriage had been nothing but a farce from the very beginning.

**A FROZEN FIRE** *by Charlotte Lamb*
What would happen to Helen's sense of duty to her blatantly unfaithful husband now that Mark Eliot had come into her life?

**TRADER'S CAY** *by Rebecca Stratton*
There was bound to be tension between Francesca and Antonio Morales, but it was Francesca's relationship with his son Andrés that caused the real trouble between the two of them ...

**KISS OF A TYRANT** *by Margaret Pargeter*
When Stacy Weldon first met Sloan Maddison he seemed decidedly antagonistic to her; yet why should he concern himself over the job his mother had offered her?

**THE LAIRD OF LOCHARRUN** *by Anne Hampson*
What had the formidable Craig Lamond been told about Lorna to make him so hostile to her?

**NO WAY OUT** *by Jane Donnelly*
Lucy's beloved twin sister had pretended to Daniel Stewart that she was in fact Lucy, and it shouldn't have been difficult for Lucy to deceive him in her turn. But ...

**THE ARRANGED MARRIAGE** *by Flora Kidd*
Roselle's marriage to Léon Chauvigny had never been a real one. Now the time had come to end it once and for all. Or had it?

**OUTBACK RUNAWAY** *by Dorothy Cork*
Running away from the heartbreak of a disastrous love affair, all Dale found was Trelawney Saber, with a bracingly unsympathetic attitude to her troubles!

**VALLEY OF THE HAWK** *by Margaret Mayo*
Damon Courtney jumped to all the wrong conclusions about Corrie — and turned her life upside down in the process!